ENCOUNTERS
with Japan

IMPRINT

ENCOUNTERS
with Japan

TWENTY EXTRAORDINARY STORIES

edited by Jennifer Duffy and Gary Anson

Angus&Robertson
An imprint of HarperCollins*Publishers*

An Angus & Robertson Publication

Angus & Robertson, an imprint of
HarperCollins *Publishers*
25 Ryde Road, Pymble, Sydney NSW 2073, Australia
31 View Road, Glenfield, Auckland 10, New Zealand

National Library of Australia
Cataloguing-in-Publication data:

Encounters with Japan: essays and stories.

ISBN 0 207 18559 X.

1. Australians—Japan—Socialisation—Anecdotes. 2. Japan—
Social life and customs—Anecdotes. I. Duffy, Jennifer.
II. Anson, Gary. III. Australia–Japan Research Centre.

952.00424

Typeset in Australia by the Australia–Japan Research Centre, Canberra.

Printed in Australia by Griffin Paperbacks, Adelaide.

9 8 7 6 5 4 3 2 1
96 95 94 9

Foreword

In January 1993, the Australia–Japan Research Centre at the Australian National University launched an essay and story competition — *Encounters with Japan* — seeking entries from Australians with experience of Japan. Entrants were encouraged to sketch a memorable incident, an interesting aspect of life in Japan, a formative encounter, or something about the experience of being an Australian in Japan. Fictitious elements were permitted, provided they were employed in a probable and realistic way.

Over 160 entries were received from Australia and Japan. All the essays were interesting and informative, and covered a wide range of experience. The pick of them appear in the collection which follows.

The Centre was fortunate in assembling a distinguished panel to judge the competition. It consisted of Dame Leonie Kramer, Chancellor, University of Sydney; Elise Tipton, Lecturer in Japanese Studies, University of Sydney; Alison Broinowski, diplomat and author; Peter Robinson, columnist, *Australian Financial Review* and *Sun Herald*; and Max Suich, editor, *Independent Monthly*. We are very grateful to the panel of judges for generously making their time available and for their enthusiasm for this project.

The panel chose the most creative and well written submissions for inclusion in a collection for publication. More difficult was the selection of the winner of the prize for the best essay — a return ticket from Australia to Japan and a week's accommodation in Tokyo. After careful consideration, the panel unanimously chose *O-Bâ-chan and the Cotton Socks* by Susan McAlister Akikusa. It is appropriate that the winning entry heads this collection.

The Centre greatly appreciates the interest and efforts of all those who took part in the contest. We are particularly grateful to Ansett Airlines for their support in funding a return air ticket to Japan to the winner.

We are also grateful to Anthony Cominos, whose proposal late in 1991 that the Centre publish a collection of essays by young Australians with study and teaching experience in Japan inspired this contest. The Australia–Japan Research Centre's primary responsibility is to undertake research work on the economic and political relationship between Australia and Japan. Hence, this collection is an unusual enterprise for the Centre but we felt that letting people speak through their impressions, rather than preparing another social scientific tract, would serve best the objective to which we were attracted. The way in which we carried the proposal forward had its particular inspiration in the collection of character sketches in Donald Richie's little volume *Different People*.

We hope that this collection will be of interest to all who want to know about how Australians respond to their encounters with Japan. The essays are a pleasure to read in themselves. They also offer insight and wisdom to all of us — students, researchers, business people, officials and travellers — all who venture forth to enjoy the interaction with Japan.

Peter Drysdale
Executive Director
Australia–Japan Research Centre

Contents

O-Bâ-chan and the Cotton Socks

Susan McAlister Akikusa

A pair of cotton socks has been my undoing.

I am guilty of the very thing that foreigners in Japan most dread: I have inadvertently done something offensive to my Japanese hosts, and deeply embarrassing to myself. I have failed to show proper respect towards my mother-in-law during her journey home. That she has been dead for four years only makes matters worse.

It is oppressively hot and humid this mid-summer's day in my mother-in-law's town, near the edge of the Kanto plain, north of Tokyo. If I peer hard enough into the heat haze through an upstairs window in the wooden house she shared with my father-in-law, I can see the blurry blue outline of mountains some miles away. The mountains, with their tall fragrant pines and deep valleys, would be cooler than the house, but we cannot go there today. For today we are to celebrate *O-Bon*, one of the most important of all Buddhist festivals, and the whole family is gathered in the house, busily preparing for my mother-in-law's homecoming.

Some days ago, my father-in-law, whom we call O-Jii-chan, 'Grandpa', took me and my husband out of the sweltering Kanto plain into the mountains and up several thousand stone steps, to show us a bridge. O-Jii-chan, who is in his seventies, mounted the worn and moss-covered steps without difficulty, but I found the climb steep and quite hard. In no time, my feet became unbearably hot inside their nylon socks, and I could feel them blistering. My father-in-law seemed determined that we should see the bridge, so I kept going, promising myself that I would give up smoking and invest in a pair of cotton socks.

The climb was worth it: looking like something out of an ancient scroll, there before us was a lovely, red, wooden bridge that curved delicately across a ravine between the mountainside and a pinnacle of rock, on which was perched a small Buddhist temple. O-Jii-chan said the bridge was important, because it had been painted by the great artist, Hokusai. When we asked how many studies Hokusai had made of the bridge, and from what angle he'd depicted it, O-Jii-chan looked puzzled, then amused. No, he explained, Hokusai hadn't done a painting of the bridge: he had painted the bridge itself, to make money before he was famous.

O-Jii-chan prayed at the temple, clapping his hands to attract the attention of its resident spirits. Afterwards, on the way down the mountain, he also stopped at a shrine dedicated to Inari, the fox-god, who watches over households and was venerated in Japan long before Buddha.

O-Jii-chan, who was born when the Meiji Emperor still ruled, has clung to the old ways, and this has no doubt helped him cope with the stupendous changes and reversals of fortune visited upon him and his country this century. He has prospered, despite earthquake, revolution, war, starvation and destitution. For his part, O-Jii-chan ascribes his durability to eating three meals of rice a day. And, for half a century, that rice was cooked by my mother-in-law, O-Bâ-chan.

The centre of one wall in O-Jii-chan's room is occupied by a shrine in which there is a photograph of O-Bâ-chan, and he kneels before it on the tatami mat and prays for her soul several times a day.

O-Bâ-chan, 'Grandma', was short like her husband, though with a face as full and round as his is square and angular. Old, prewar photographs show a matronly woman in a formal black *kimono* bearing the family crest, her hair pulled back into a bun, her expression serious, almost stern, in its composure. Only a suggestion of uncertainty, a slightly quizzical cast to her brows, belies the overall impression of matriarchal dignity. This is a woman proud of her three sons and two daughters, but unable to completely disguise her perennial unease about what they might be up to.

As the years went by, and Japan re-invented itself, O-Bâ-chan's appearance also changed. She may never have been able to bring herself to actually smile at the camera, but in a major concession to the postwar era, she was occasionally photographed wearing Western-style clothes. One of the last pictures taken of O-Bâ-chan shows her sitting in a paddle float, off Waikiki beach. She is wearing a swimming costume and a floppy hat, but she is not smiling.

O-Jii-chan now lives with his oldest son, daughter-in-law and two grandsons, but he misses O-Bâ-chan, and seems frequently to be lonely. He feels the younger generation does not always show him sufficient respect, and he appears especially disconcerted by his jeans and Walkman-clad grandsons, who are twice as tall as he is. So the festival of *O-Bon*, when he can bring his wife home for a little while, is precious to him.

And, today is *O-Bon*. In the kitchen, where the heat is so intense I am surprised the microwave does not melt, my sisters-in-law are readying the traditional food to be presented to O-Bâ-chan later that day. I feel awkward, because I do not know how to help, and because my energetic and well-groomed sisters-in-law seem untouched by the heat, whereas I am nearly supine. My feet are still blistered and hurting from the Hokusai bridge and subsequent excursions, and I remind myself that, before the day is out, I must buy some cotton socks.

The menfolk are sitting around the kitchen table while the women work. This is traditional. However, when my brother-in-law says a cup of coffee would be welcome, his wife points to the coffee pot and politely suggests he make some. This is not how things were done in O-Jii-chan's day, and he looks bemused. O-Bâ-chan certainly would not have approved. My husband recalls that when he was a boy, he liked to go shopping with his mother, which was bad enough, and then help her prepare meals, which was worse. O-Bâ-chan tried turning him out of her kitchen, but he kept coming back and cooking things, and she lived in perpetual fear of the neighbours finding out.

The whole family agrees that O-Bâ-chan was a great shopper. She shopped every day for food, like all good Japanese housewives do. During the war, when the family lived in Manchuria, she had ample scope for bargaining and bartering in the small stores which lined the cobbled streets of Harbin. And she certainly knew a thing or two about shopping for clothes, because when O-Jii-chan got out of the army, he set himself up as a purveyor of *kimonos* to the Japanese community in Manchuria. They did very well, for a time. Long before many a military and political leader in Tokyo grasped what was happening, O-Bâ-chan realised the war was going badly for Japan and the days of its empire were numbered, because Chinese boys had begun to beat up her sons on their way to school.

O-Bâ-chan's family, like the country as a whole, somehow managed to survive the grim times that followed. I am aware that there are no photographs from this period. There is one legacy, however: my husband's sweet tooth, which he attributes to the chocolate bars handed out to him and his starving siblings by concerned American soldiers.

Eventually, the family prospered. The big department stores of postwar Japan offered O-Bâ-chan an undreamt of cornucopia of goods, while at the same time severely limiting her scope for bargaining and bartering. However, she satisfied her need to demonstrate thrift, and to personalise the shopping process, by exclaiming that every item that caught her attention was *takai*, expensive.

After I married into the family, various members confided to me that O-Bâ-chan could be quite loud sometimes. This is not how a Japanese woman is meant to be. In particular, she had a big, deep laugh, which used to burst from her at inappropriate times, most notably during important social and religious ceremonies. It seems likely that her grave and respectable demeanour, so evident in photographs, was in large measure assiduously maintained to compensate for such a disturbingly unfeminine trait. No one in her family can recall that O-Bâ-chan had a particularly well-developed sense of humour, so these outbursts may often have reflected simple nervousness, or some deeper reaction to what was, after all, the rather confining life of an old style Japanese wife and mother.

O-Bâ-chan was gossiping on the telephone when death came, suddenly, like her laugh. She was cremated and her ashes laid to rest in a cemetery some distance from her home, and O-Jii-chan's loneliness began.

But, today he is happy because it is *O-Bon*, and his wife is coming home again.

All over Japan, families are gathering to receive the dead back into their homes. It is a holiday, a welcome event in the midst of the long and stiflingly humid Japanese summer, and while gifts of rice flour dumplings, noodles, vegetables, fruit and water are offered to the dead, the living also partake of good food and drink and gossip, not all of it about the dear departed.

It seems to me that the Japanese are particularly mindful of the spirit world in summer. Perhaps it is the long evenings and the play of lamplight and moonlight, or the humid nights of restless sleep and wakefulness, when the strange sounds of nocturnal creatures come clearly through thin wooden walls and paper screens. My husband claims that summer became ghost time simply because, before the advent of air conditioning, hearing a spooky tale was an effective way of cooling down.

He says no one is certain how *O-Bon*, the Festival of the Dead, began, but it is generally thought to have come to Japan with Buddhism and was happily adopted by the ancestor-worshipping Japanese. According to tradition, after the mother of one of Buddha's disciples died, he had a dream in which he saw her in great agony, begging him for help. She was stranded in the netherworld without food or water, and she was starving. So the good son prepared food for his mother and ventured into the netherworld, to bring it to her. *O-Bon* is held to commemorate this filial devotion, and to ensure that no other spirit is left without sustenance.

O-Jii-chan is reverential, but also quite excited, as he places food on a tray for his wife, and gives a final inspection to the lamp in which O-Bâ-chan's spirit will be carried home. I am touched that he has asked me to accompany him and my husband to the cemetery to collect her. It is my husband who conveys O-Jii-chan's wishes to me, not because of etiquette, but to avoid misunderstanding. There is goodwill on both sides, but my father-in-law and I have some trouble communicating. He doesn't understand English, and can't, or won't, understand my Japanese, because I am not Japanese and it therefore stands to reason that I cannot speak the language. I am a *gaijin*, a foreigner, and so he speaks to me in Chinese and Russian, which are *gaijin* languages, and which I must therefore be able to understand. I don't, but we muddle through somehow.

We put on our shoes as we leave the house, and the pain this causes me acts as a reminder to buy some cotton socks before I attempt any further expeditions on foot.

At the cemetery, we tidy O-Bâ-chan's grave and put fresh flowers on it. Using a long-handled bamboo ladle, we pour a cooling stream of water over her headstone and place the tray of food at its base. O-Jii-chan prays, and then places the lamp on his wife's grave. He holds a taper to the wick and a little flame springs up, showing that O-Bâ-chan's spirit has been caught. Carefully shielding the flame, O-Jii-chan carries the lamp back to the car, and we set off home.

It is not until we pass an open department store that I remember we are going on another long walk the next morning, and my need for suitable footwear is becoming urgent. I therefore ask my husband whether, should O-Jii-chan have no objection, we can stop at the store and get some cotton socks.

O-Jii-chan sounds horrified. '*Ii-e*', he says, 'No, no, no!', shaking his head and clutching the lamp and O-Bâ-chan's spirit close to his chest. He gesticulates forcefully towards the road ahead and tells my husband to drive on.

It suddenly occurs to me that I have offended O-Jii-chan on this most special of days. I am mortified. How could I allow my wretched feet to intrude upon this most special and touching of homecomings? How could I even contemplate visiting a department store while on an errand of such spiritual and emotional importance? I have failed to live up to expectations, and for the rest of the journey I sit, silent, despondent, and severely humbled, in the back of the car. Up till now, I have fancied myself as rather adept at avoiding the much-vaunted pitfalls of East–West relations.

Once home, O-Jii-chan and his wife's spirit quickly disappear into his room, as though fearful of the *gaijin* once more trying to waylay them or debase the occasion. I avert my eyes from my mother-in-law's picture hanging on the wall, convinced her gaze is even sterner than usual.

Some time later, I ask my husband to speak to O-Jii-chan on my behalf, to apologise and try to explain my crass behaviour. Looking somewhat puzzled, my husband sets off, only to return after a few minutes. He appears unconcerned.

'Well', he says, 'I spoke to O-Jii-chan and he was surprised that you felt you had to apologise. He certainly wasn't insulted'.

I am stunned. 'But, what about the way he clasped the lamp when I suggested going to the department store? And, he was so adamant we couldn't stop! He's just being polite. I know I spoilt O-Bâ-chan's homecoming, I dishonoured her spirit!'

My husband smiles. 'Not at all. O-Jii-chan was a bit alarmed, not offended. He didn't mind you wanting to buy some socks. You see, the problem was this: O-Jii-chan said he knew that if O-Bâ-chan's spirit had seen you going into the department store, she'd have followed you, and that would have been that. He would never have got her out again.'

That night, I dream I hear O-Bâ-chan laughing.

American DJ

Anthony Connell

You don't need me to tell you about how wonderful Japanese people can be, how kind and how caring. There will be plenty of people to back me up on that, at length. And plenty of people who've come across garden-variety racism, as well. But what I want to tell you about is the dark side of that nation, the part that most Japanese themselves like to pretend isn't there. I want to tell you about my time with the *yakuza*, the Japanese mafia.

Six years ago, at the age of twenty-one, I was in Japan learning how to survive on a working holiday visa (and very little else). Working in Tokyo was not what I thought it would be. English teachers may be highly paid, but how many times can you ask, 'Is this a pen?' without going nuts. Just once I would've liked someone to say, 'Of course it's a bloody pen. Say something interesting will you!'. Even in Japanese. But no, back would come the answer, 'Yes, it's a pen'. In fact, any conversation in Japanese would have been heavensent, since that's why I went to Japan in the first place, not to pick up my flatmate's American accent.

So it was that I found myself answering an advertisement for an 'American DJ' to work in a small country town. I had experience back in Australia on volunteer radio, and I used to work as a mobile disc jockey. I was young, I was cool, and I was keen to be out where no one spoke English and I couldn't help but learn Japanese. Hey, I was perfect for the job. Yes, I know, I seemed to have missed the obvious fact that I'm not an American, but Japanese can't tell us apart anyway. We all look the same to them.

The interviewer was the boss of the disco, and a few other businesses as well. He looked the part in his grey pinstripe suit and diamond stickpin. Even his hair was slicked back. We got the negotiations out of the way pretty quickly — he'd provide accommodation; I'd work six nights a week. Then he asked for my passport to check my visa details. Yep, you guessed it, there is a way for them to tell us apart! But after some further negotiation my nationality wasn't a problem either. I promised to dye my hair blond and he seemed to think a blond Australian was as good as an American any day of the week.

When I arrived in Hamamatsu I was met at the station by a long, black, stretch limousine. This is the way to live, I thought, as the white-gloved driver cruised the few short blocks to the office. The first thing I had to do was meet the *buchô*, 'department manager', and be reimbursed for my fare from Tokyo. I tried not to stare at the man, who had obviously been in some kind of awful accident. A long, angry scar ran from his right cheekbone, down across his mouth to his chin. I felt sorry for him that it had healed so badly. He seemed a very cold and efficient man, and I wondered if the scar had changed his personality for the worse. Then I saw his wife. She had the *same* scar in the *same* place. That was when I started to think something was strange.

Soon I was driven to nearby Toyohashi — a rural backwater, population one million. The *tenchô,* 'club manager', of the Toyohashi disco was missing two knuckle joints on the little finger of his left hand, and even I in my youthful ignorance knew this was a sign of the *yakuza.* What I didn't know was how the *yakuza* operate, or I would've jumped out of the car right then. The police turning up on the first night should have been a warning too, but when you're young you think you're invulnerable. Why mince words; when you're young you're stupid.

Not that I had any reason to be nervous. Everyone at the club was great. I asked the *tenchô* about his finger (or lack of one) and he explained that he used to be a *yakuza* but was now reformed. He might as well have said that he used to be alive, but was now dead, since the chances of that being true were just as slim. The *yakuza* don't operate that way, but I didn't know it then. Even the kitchen staff were gang members. The old cook was one. His wife helped in the kitchen too, and one night she showed me her thighs, which had been tattooed from knee to waist. When she was young she served drinks kneeling in the formal *seiza* position, and drew up her *kimono* to allow customers to admire the beauty and the workmanship. 'When she was young' would have been before the war, so it was hard to see the beauty, but I doubt the customers were looking at the pictures anyway.

And, of course, there were the other foreigners working there — three Filipina waitresses and the previous 'American' DJ, George. I got the job because George wasn't American enough, although he held a US passport. He claimed to be of Polish descent, though one of the girls said he had confessed to being a KGB defector, placed in Japan by the US for his own protection. I believe that was true, but I don't expect you to. I don't have time to go into George's story here; suffice to say he was weird. Ever seen anyone try to dance a Russian (Polish?) folk dance to the tune of Bananarama's 'Venus'? Not a pretty sight.

The waitresses were nothing more than that. They weren't expected to go home with customers; they just poured drinks, laughed at jokes, and danced if customers wanted to. They weren't stupid either. One of them had a degree from a Manila university and had thrown in her job in the international department of a bank to come to Japan. She made three times the salary she used to make at home. And they were fun; they taught me Japanese, they even taught me a little Tagalog. Loui was the cutest, and I had a crush on her. I liked it there.

Our customers were few. The charms of Loui and the other Filipina girls managed to hold a few regulars, small-time businessmen and shop-owners mostly, with the occasional chicken farmer sneaking a night off from the wife. These farmers felt it was exciting, somehow dangerous, to be in a gang-run club with what they were sure were 'women of the water world'; prostitutes, and available. The real prostitutes were down the road and Japanese, but the world is how you see it, right? One of the regulars did manage to bed one of the girls (I think), but only after buying presents for what sounded like her entire extended family. The girls lived next door to me in an apartment provided by the Boss, so I'm not guessing here — they were honest.

The customers I really liked were the ones who came to dance, not just to make suggestive banter with the waitresses. They were few, but they were closer to my age and they were definitely interesting. Dancing in Japan isn't what it is in Australia. I was impressed by the full-length mirrors all along one wall of the club, until I had to clean them, but they are vital in Japanese discos. A gang of schoolkids, aged fifteen and sixteen, would hit the club some nights, and they'd all face the mirror in rows, ranked according to skill with the worst at the front, never taking their eyes off the leader as they struggled to match his steps. They all went to the same school, and dancing to Eurobeat must have been their definition of cool. No better example have I seen of the Japanese group than this; twenty or more earnest kids, the weaker among them being helped by the best, moving in unison to a jackhammer beat with not a foot out of place.

Fair enough, they were just kids. Underage and illegally on the premises, but still kids. The *tenchô* wouldn't serve them anything harder than orange juice, which goes to show that not all *yakuza* are heartless drug-pushers. And while they weren't exactly representative of the Japanese club-going community as a whole, your average adult was little different. Alone, they would dance with the mirror. In couples, they would dance with the mirror. Maybe they feel no guilt in Japan for this self-adoration. Maybe they wanted to check that they weren't making fools of themselves (not a bad idea for a lot of Aussie clubs). Maybe they were bored.

Bored, perhaps, but not all boring. One young driver used to come in and cut a mean rug, twisting and moving real smooth. He never stayed long, and I thought: this guy's cool.

One night he came in with his little finger wrapped in a pristine white bandage, and being one bourbon down and thinking he was a friend after the three or four times we'd talked, I joked, 'What happened? Accident?'.

He didn't say anything. I knew that he'd lopped off his own fingertip, that he had to be *yakuza*; I'm not ignorant. I'm just big-mouthed and stupid. One of the girls grabbed me by the arm and had me out of sight around the corner fast. I went back to spinning records and they kept him distracted until he forgot me. Those girls were real professionals at managing people.

Another young guy who came in was with the mob, too. Muscular, he danced like he knew he was good, like he was the Chosen One. Between my pidgin Japanese, his twenty-five words of English and some imaginative gesturing, we managed to make each other laugh, quite a few times. I liked him. He said he was a *samurai*, and I asked the *tenchô* about him later, not really believing that this Japanese version of the neighbourhood larrikin could claim descent from the ruling classes. It seems he was telling the truth, at least as far as the modern *yakuza* definition goes. A *samurai*, explained the *tenchô*, is gangland parlance for the fighter who represents his faction in territorial and power disputes. To avoid scenes like the Valentine's Day massacre, the gang leaders decide to settle things in a civilised manner, if you can call ten-inch blades civilised. They face off their man against the opposition's, and while raking off profits from the side bets, they settle the dispute. The fights are almost always to first blood, though more serious problems can call for a fight to the death.

Although still a bit dubious, I did tone down my jokes with him. I was just starting to get casual again when one night he came in roaring drunk, and weaving to a table, dropped his arm on the glass top. It must have hurt, because he had a cut which ran from the back of his wrist two-thirds of the way up his forearm. Actually, thinking about it now, it's not impossible that it was self-inflicted, but he wasn't the sort. Anyway, he was there, and he was there to dance, so he grabbed one of the girls and started rocking around on his Cuban heels, half swagger and half stagger. Almost immediately the wound sprang open. Blood oozed down his arm, but he didn't notice; he kept on swinging it while the blood dripped patterns on the floor. The girl he was dancing with shrieked and did a curious dance herself, alternating between jumping back with her hand over her mouth and jumping forward wanting to help him.

Finally, he seemed to feel it, or noticed the wetness over the effects of the alcohol anyway, and the girls bundled him off to the toilets to clean up his arm. Rivulets of blood ran black down his hand under the fluoro lighting. The music never missed a beat, and he emerged five minutes later with his arm glowing white. They had improvised with toilet paper, and as he poured another drink, the first dark patches of blood seeped through. He couldn't stay still though, and with toilet paper trailing like a mummy's wrapping, he hit the floor again.

Somehow I couldn't think of that guy as evil, as scary. Yet there was one night that left a sour taste in my mouth, and had me wanting to get out. One smelly, raggedy long-distance truck driver rolled into the bar on an otherwise quiet midweek night. He was friendly, real friendly. He was high, real high. And he told us all about it, like he was sharing a joke. The way you could get stuff from the *yakuza* anywhere; they had it all. The way you could fool the police anytime; just look at this, and he pulled out an eyedropper 'Brand X Cleareyes', or the Japanese equivalent. Great, I thought, now you can get whacked off your face with eyedrops. What next?

'Looks like a regular eyedropper, right?', he said, smug, with the look of someone who knows he's got your interest. With a flourish only slightly shaky, he untwisted the rubber nipple and unsheathed that horrible, still-moist surprise. A needle, a syringe, thick enough to see the ellipse of the angular cut at its tip. Flashing in the red disco lights, double threaded so it screwed back in, an innocent eyedropper became a pump to inject its contents into eager veins.

Not long after, his pleasure faded at having so easily shocked us, he disappeared into the toilets. He was in there five whole minutes, just long enough for me to overwrite all those stories I'd heard of a drug-free, safe Japan; just long enough for me to make my decision to move on.

Of course, you can't just leave the *yakuza* that easily. It took me a month to let them know, to make my excuses. I was called to Hamamatsu to see the Boss. I was nervous, but it turned out there was no need to be concerned. He simply had a business proposition to make — I find him dancers to work in his clubs and I get 600 bucks for every girl I deliver. 'No', I said, 'I don't think so'. 'More for blondes of course', he countered, thinking I was just holding out.

Finally he understood I wasn't going to be in it. Fine to play with my own life, standing up for yourself is only natural. No way was I going to put girls over here, even if they thought they knew the score. I would be responsible, and after all I'd learned in four months in the underbelly of Japan, I was not going to stand up against the *yakuza*. This was to be the last time I would.

Samurai in Cheap Socks

Ian Hamilton

I lay spread-eagled in my best blue business suit on the *tatami* mat, arm-wrestling a *geisha*.

A pretty woman, her face whitened in the traditional manner, her black wig exquisitely decorated, she was as strong as a young ox. She threw me a sweet smile, the way she had been winning me all night.

Did gallantry demand I let her win?

But even as the thought formed she read it and graciously allowed her wrist to flutter gently down to touch the *tatami*.

Her little game was over in fits of giggles for us both, and howls of laughter from around the room, the loudest from my own lady, Alana, witness to it all and probably, perversely, wishing to see me lose to the younger woman.

But no game is ever really over in Japan.

Shinjo-san, our host for the weekend, a man a good twenty and more years older than me and who barely reached my shoulder, erupted in roars of delight and promptly took the *geisha*'s place, his smile almost as wide as his stocky shoulders as he snugged down on the floor, our forearms touching.

He was just an old man who ran his family's *sake* brewery, elbows out of his sweater and wearing baggy pants, and over that the warrior outfit he had earlier borrowed from the older of the two *geisha*.

Our hands clasped. We took the pressure against each other.

Okay, old man, I may have a good bellyful of your new season's *sake* but you are far older and there's not much of you. Wham. My wrist hit the *tatami*. No moment for gallantry here.

The fact that this old man could heft a sixty kilogram bag of rice above his short-cropped grey head, when about the only thing I heft all day is a ballpoint pen, had at least a little to do with his victory over me.

Shinjo-san helped me to my feet, hugged me with open affection, for a second it almost seemed he was about to kiss me, and then he demanded more *sake* all round, with an especially large tot for the vanquished.

The young *geisha* helped me courteously back to my cushion alongside Alana, now red-faced and speechless with mirth. Possibly red-faced with a drop too much *sake*, too.

Still in his crazy warrior clothes, Shinjo-san took up a sword so sharp you could shave your teeth on it after a heavy night like this and pranced about the *ryokan*'s party room striking theatrical poses, singing an ancient song that the older *geisha* quickly took up on the *shamisen*, his strong voice coming from deep in his gut as he slashed at the air with the terrifying sword, missing the paper *shôji* screens by millimetres.

He went into a long recital, which our friend Matsuo-san whispered to us was a story of the sadness of battle, and he ended by laying down his sword before us and bowing deeply.

God, he was more entertaining than the *geisha* he had hired to amuse us for the night.

In the West, the odd client had been known to buy me a sandwich for goodwill. One brought me dinner, once. But Shinjo-san, now here was a man who knew how to show his thanks.

We had filled our happy faces with sweet local river carp washed down with *miso* soup and followed with king prawns from the coast, delicate pork *tonkatsu*, Japanese spinach with dried bonito flakes, wonderfully flavoursome rice dusted with spices and herbs, a large shellfish steamed in soy sauce, assorted vegetables with a dash of *sake* and other adventurous and mysterious things, all chased down with tiny bottomless cups of his very best fresh *sake*.

And lying beside us, congealing to death and untouched, were two enormous plates of steak and eggs; he had researched what Australians reputedly eat most. We didn't. His choice was not our choice. But his effort to please was overwhelming.

Shinjo-san, one in a long family line who owned a *sake* brewery in Aizu-Wakamatsu, in chilly Fukushima Prefecture, a very traditional man in a most traditional Japanese business, had approached me and my Japanese crew to apply Western communication skills to reposition one of his *sake* brands in the marketplace; he wanted us to do for him the kinds of things we know how to do for soap and cereal, beer and peanut butter. We did that. And it worked. His appreciation seemed to have no bounds. A tough and clever man, financially successful, he had clearly never for a moment lost sight of the truly good things in life.

Alana fell head over heels in love with him the moment she met him. I just plainly adored him. I always will.

How can you not love a man who feeds you well, amuses you constantly, pays you on time without quibble, is extravagant with his praise, and is endlessly playful?

In open-fronted green plastic slippers, in freezing temperatures, he had taken us up and down all over his old *sake* brewery in the early morning, our toes almost left behind like little icy nodules on the cold, wet floor.

He tied an orange sweat rag around his head, some kind of symbol of his work ethic, wearing it only inside the brewery; the rest of the time it waved out of his hip pocket.

He shared all of his secrets with us. He had us taste and smell and begin to learn to understand the rice fermenting in long trays.

He told us how, every night during this season of producing the new *sake*, he slept alongside the *kôji*, the malted rice, waking every hour or so to feel it in his hand, to test it against his nose and lips.

Alana asked why he, not one of his workers, should spend the night on the floor?

He told her, in honest surprise at her question, 'If you fear your children may be sick in the night, you sleep beside them, don't you?'

That was an answer a mother could fully appreciate. Her eyes reflected her own memories at his response.

That night at his party he told us how he had visited France many times and made friends of certain vignerons, not from any desire to make wine but to commune with fellow artists. With joy on his face he talked of the gratification that comes from taking a simple growing thing, a common grape or a plain kernel of rice, and turning it into a wonderment.

And here he was, the mad *samurai* in cheap socks, the point of his sword flashing over my head at the speed of polished lightning, reducing even the two *geisha*, professional entertainers, to a desperate case of laughter sickness.

And they tell me the Japanese are a very serious people. Hah!

There were quieter moments that evening as the *sake* took its mellow effect.

Shinjo-san explained to us how it is unlikely that a *gaijin* would successfully do business in Japan without knowing the Japanese.

As he put it: 'To understand a Japanese, you must know his ancestors'.

He talked about his town and its role in Japan's civil war 140 years ago; of the teenage boys and girls whose names are still recalled in songs and stories, who had taken their own lives in sight of Tsuruga Castle rather than be defeated.

'When I speak of war in Aizu-Wakamatsu, I don't mean World War II, I mean the civil war.'

My own father may well have focused Shinjo-san in his gunsights once or twice.

Shinjo-san may well have squeezed off a few angry bursts at My Old Man.

They had both been devoted airmen working the same patch out of Papua New Guinea. I was happy they'd missed each other, that both were still alive and well. They both came back from it. I wished, deep, deep down, that Old Syd could have left his Queensland beach and been with us this night, but in a funny way he was there anyway.

For me, war was Korea, and later Vietnam. Every generation has its own wars to remember. For Shinjo-san it was not the war he had been to, it was the war that had the most meaning for himself and his town. He made me think I should learn again from Gallipoli. He gave me perspective because he had it to give.

Shinjo-san composed a *tanka* for the two of us and I troubled Matsuo-san later to explain to me that a *tanka* is always spoken with precisely seventeen syllables in three lines before a breath pause, followed by fourteen syllables in two lines; not an easy morsel to throw together in a hurry in any language, nor a quick formula to recall after drinking *sake* all night.

Maybe, unless you're an old aviator with a pilot's sharp memory for checklists. I hold a great regard for stick and rudder people.

Some people throw all they have into every tiny thing they do. Shinjo-san bought himself a speedboat to go waterskiing on nearby Lake Inawashiro in summer, but, he told us, 'My staff loved watching me so much, they would come out to see me, and I was embarrassed, so I gave them the speedboat'.

He did it all over again when he took up tennis: now his employees own the tennis court.

Nursing ourselves back to life in our private *o-furo* early next morning, just our eyes and noses showing like crocodiles in a creek, the scalding water melting away our trivial hangovers, we agreed that neither of us had ever before met anybody quite like Mr Shinjo, on the surface a simple countryman who makes *sake* for a living.

Good *sake*.

My First Rush Hour

Marie-Jeanne Johnson

When I first came to Japan, I lived up in the farm country of Fukushima, where the air is clear and the sidewalks come in at ten o'clock, an hour earlier than in the rest of the country. The local dialect is incomprehensible, even to other Japanese, and the only other *gaijin* around are the Mormon missionaries on the main street, with their sincere suits and fresh apple-pie faces. I lived rent-free with an acquaintance from home, whose presence there was one of the reasons I had chosen Fukushima in the first place.

The other reason was that I was terrified of Tokyo. On my few trips through the city I had been overwhelmed, both emotionally and physically, by the sheer mass of people on the sidewalks and in the trains. Unfortunately, my Tokyo friends lived on the Odakyu line, which currently is a neck and neck contender with the Chuo line in the dubious category of 'most crowded trains, at all times, in greater Tokyo'. Like veterans swapping battle stories, the residents of southwest Tokyo like to boast of the horrors they have endured on their respective train lines. I listened to their sagas of sleeves ripped off in the exiting scrum and long hair trapped in closing doors, and became convinced that living in Tokyo counts for a couple of centuries off your time in Purgatory and that *I* wanted no part of it.

(My favourite rush-hour horror story, though not particularly horrific, is nonetheless such a typical piece of Japonica that I can't resist repeating it. Apparently some determined young type was trying to elbow his way into a car already filled to 250 per cent capacity. The woman he was attempting to displace, who asserted her own right of entry to the extent that her fingertips were on the inside of the door frame, curtly suggested that he wait for the next train. At this the young man bridled and spat out the ultimate insult: 'You work for an unimportant company!').

However, the day eventually came when I had to board the Yamanote line at rush hour. True, it was *late* rush hour, just on nine o'clock, and it was only for four stops, but I was still dreading the prospect all the way down from Fukushima. I had taken the morning *shinkansen* express, a fast ninety-minute trip spent standing, since I wasn't going to pay for a reserved seat, and the *jiyûseki*, the unreserved seats, were all taken. Now, I didn't in the least mind standing for an hour and a half, since the lack of *jiyûseki* on the *shinkansen* is just part of the nature of things, but the idea of the perhaps ten-minute ride from Ueno station to Tokyo station reduced me to pulp.

Well, I reached Ueno and got on the Yamanote. Everyone else got on the Yamanote too. It wasn't exactly subway packer time, meaning I could still breathe reasonably freely, but it was much more crowded than a train at home ever gets, than a train at home would ever be *allowed* to get, with people pressed close in front and behind and on both sides.

More and more people got on and my anxiety level grew; and then an odd thing happened. When we reached the point where there *were* no more inches, or even centimetres, between the bodies and we were all touching each other someplace, everyone relaxed, and a sudden wave of friendliness swept through the car. Over to my left a woman began a laughing conversation with the two strangers beside her, and a couple of guys a few feet away on the other side started to joke among themselves: '*Jama no te*', one of them punned untranslatably; since '*jama*' means nuisance, it could be rendered as 'strain train' or some such thing. Tension almost visibly drained from the air. My shoulders, which had been hunched up somewhere around my ears, returned to their normal level, and I found myself smiling.

When we started off it was even better. It was like a waterbed, held on all sides by a strong soft surface that gave but still supported. The train went forward and we all leaned on the people behind us; it pulled up and we all leaned on the people in front. There was no possibility of falling, since there was nowhere to fall. It was fun, it was exhilarating, and it satisfied, in a very basic way, some sort of need I hadn't been aware I'd had.

Before coming to Japan, I had worked in daycare for ten years. Then my back gave out, and I'd had to quit and find less strenuous teaching work elsewhere. But it seems I had been missing the sort of constant body contact I had had with the kids and the staff at my old workplace, that 'skinship' which the Japanese like to talk about so much. That ten minutes on the Yamanote line was one of the most affirmative experiences I had in the country, and it makes me wonder. Like most Western countries, and unlike many Asian ones, in Japan you usually have to pay if you want to be touched. But unlike most Westerners, the Japanese spend the first two or three years of their lives being carried around on their mother's back, living constantly with the feel of another's body and another's warmth during the day and sleeping between Mama and Papa at night. And then it all ends, around the age of five or six. Virtually no more touching until adulthood and marriage, and then only in private and quite often only in bed. You'd think they'd go into skin withdrawal, as I had. And so I have to wonder if, protestations to the contrary, the famous packed subways of Tokyo are not, fundamentally, the way the Japanese like it.

Or maybe there's another ethos at work entirely. When the doors opened at each station there were none of those famous mob scenes that I had heard about, just an orderly and mass evacuation. At the stop after Ueno, however, instead of the usual ten or twenty people getting off, there was only one woman, and it was interesting to see how she managed the feat of manoeuvring through a dense crowd and out the door.

Unfortunately, English isn't very good for describing what she did. Basically, she just moved through the crowd and got off. Yes, but think what that means. Obviously she exerted pressure on the bodies in front of her to make the physical room to fit her own body in, but she wasn't pushing as we understand the term. And while everybody else was in her way, with virtually no space left to get out of her way, no one was actually blocking her. We were all just there, and she was just moving through us, causing us to be constricted a little more than we already were. No offence in the world, either offered or taken.

This is simply not possible in the West, where the close proximity of strangers involves an automatic imputation of malice and consequent hostility. However much my head understands that people on a crowded subway have no choice but to come into 'my' space, my gut registers their physical encroachment as an attack. That's why the crowds of Tokyo arouse such unreasoning fury in Westerners.

The very phrase 'You're in my way' is sufficient illustration of our attitude that space is the property of one person, that one person being me. A crowd in the West consists of a number of individuals generally at odds with each other: me and them. A crowd in Japan consists of us. Space is just space, and belongs to everybody. There is only one way, and we are all in it, rather than all of us having our own personal ways which must be defended to the death. The Japanese attitude is not only more tolerant and less egocentric than ours, it sometimes, as on the Yamanote line, seems to approach a Zen ability to not-be, which is unknown to us. I don't often find the Japanese particularly Zen-like, but it *is* part of their culture.

And, of course, I have to add that the exhilaration of my first experience has rarely been repeated. Maybe the reason is that, when I finally moved to Tokyo, I lived on the western half of the Yamanote line and had to deal with people a social cut or two below the well-trained suits who work in the major firms headquartered near Tokyo station. I don't know.

But that first glimpse of another way of being, of the group identity at work, provided a hint that I subsequently followed in my daily encounters with the hordes of Tokyo, and I'm willing to pass it on to others for whatever it may be worth.

In Nagoya Castle there are English maps showing the floor you're on and a red arrow indicating your present location, and underneath that, instead of the usual 'You are here', is the rather unexpected: 'Here we are'. It's not a bad motto for a commuter in Tokyo. When I go through Shinjuku station at eight in the morning with the other half million people who are doing the same thing — when I have to queue to go through the turnstiles, queue to go up the stairs, queue to get on the train, queue to get off the train, queue to go down the stairs, queue to go out the turnstiles, and queue to go out of the station — then, pushing my awareness a few notches along in the direction of universal consciousness, I think: 'Here we are'. And so, matching my footsteps to those of the *sarariman* on the step above me, I become one with the crowd as we flow onto the Yamanote platform.

Living in Moon Tree Hill

Hilary Rumley

Moon Tree Hill. That's the literal translation of the name of our neighbourhood in the greater Tokyo area. Its meaning is obscure, even to long-term residents. But there is a low hill, or rather a ridge-like embankment, on the other side of the small, sluggish river beside our apartment block which forms the boundary between Kawasaki and Yokohama. And there are cherry trees on the embankment, as well as a grove of tall old pines which surround a local shrine on top of the ridge, quite clearly visible from our apartment. I like to think the name of our neighbourhood might have something to do with these trees on this hill. It would still be a pleasant place for moon-viewing on a clear autumn night.

Our apartment is quite small, but convenient and bright. Dennis arrived before the children and I and had to begin furnishing the apartment completely from scratch: curtains, refrigerator, ceiling light fittings, gas stove top, washing machine, basic furniture . . . Construction of our block had been completed only a few months earlier, and he was the first occupant of this particular ground floor apartment. Lack of ventilation over the humid summer months meant that the brand new *tatami* mats in two rooms had become completely covered with mould and had to be thoroughly scrubbed before the apartment could be occupied. 'How did you know what to use?' I asked Dennis later, after realising the difficulty of deciphering the labels on just about everything, especially cleaning products. 'Someone at work told me what to buy. They wrote the Japanese word for "cleaner-for-removing-mould-from-tatami-matting" ', he said, 'so I went and bought it'.

It took us a while to get used to a few features of our apartment and some of the newly-acquired appliances. We were mystified by the high technology involved in heating the bath water to the desired temperature. A helpful neighbour was happy to show us how the push-button electronic, thermostatic, gas hot-water system worked. Soaking in a scalding hot bath on a cold winter evening has now become compulsive. The same neighbour also patiently explained the Japanese instructions on the washing machine and the rice cooker.

The extent of storage space, even in a small apartment like ours, is quite impressive, as is the design of the toilet cistern, the top of which doubles as a hand washing bowl after flushing. The paper-covered sliding screens on cupboards and between rooms are light, elegant and convenient, yet relatively easy to damage, as we have found out to our cost. Inspired by the latest *sumo* tournament, Dennis and the children were having a few friendly bouts when one of them put a foot through a screen door. Another time I awoke startled from a dream and did the same thing. We're told they can be easily re-papered when tenancies change, but if the same paper design is not available, all the screens have to be re-done, not just the damaged ones.

Futons. Bedding. There's a lot of conventional wisdom about *futons* which I've gradually learned, some by observation and some in the form of direct advice and admonishment from my concerned neighbours. Ideally, a good Japanese housewife waits until all family members have left for the day, listens to the weather forecast, puts the *futons* out to air over the balcony railings and is sure to be home by mid-afternoon to bring them in. On a fine morning *futons* are usually draped over railings around nine and brought back in again around four. Special *futon* clamps are used to prevent *futons* from being blown off balconies in strong gusts of wind. One morning, we retrieved the pillow of an upstairs neighbour from our balcony. Before being brought back inside, *futons* are generally given a good whacking with a special implement that looks like an old-fashioned carpet beater. Airing the *futons* has several benefits apart from the general freshening effect. The sun and fresh air heat and fluff up the inner material, making the *futons* even more warm and comfortable at night. It's essential, I've been told, to bring *futons* inside before there's any chance of them getting damp. People in lower level apartments should bring their *futons* in earlier than people higher up in order to avoid all the dust that will inevitably settle as *futons* above are given their daily beating.

Most mornings, not being able to understand the Japanese weather forecast, I glance at the other balconies to see if everyone else's *futons* are out or not, and then I follow suit. Our *futons* are invariably airing for longer than ideal. I've often found myself at varying distances from home, keeping a wary eye on the weather and hoping that one of us will be back in time to bring them in. One Sunday, when we were away until nearly dark, my anxiety about the *futons* was increasing in direct proportion to the growth of ominous black clouds which had begun to appear. I needn't have worried. By the time we got home, our *futons* had been removed from our balcony railings, carefully folded and wrapped in plastic sheeting. 'I put your mattress on second floor's landing because of rain' stated a note on our door signed by Mrs Kobayashi from a fifth floor apartment.

Another neighbour once told me some cautionary tales about *futons* being on the receiving end of spit and vomit from above. She also told me about someone she knew whose *futons* were accidentally set on fire by upstairs smokers. One day, after a period of prolonged rain, and obviously concerned about the state of our unaired *futons*, she invited me into her apartment to demonstrate how her electric *futon*-airer works. It's like a small reverse vacuum cleaner with a large nylon sack, which is placed between top and bottom *futon*. When the machine is switched on, the sack fills with warm air. Airing the *futon* this way takes about an hour. My neighbour insisted on lending it to me. The effect of the *futon*-airer was amazing. The thought crossed my mind that for Japanese wives whose husbands are regularly home later than midnight, a *futon*-airer is quite a reasonable substitute for a warm body.

• • •

Our immediate women neighbours, some of whom fortunately speak quite good English, were happy to provide us with information about our apartment block and neighbourhood. Mrs Morimoto explained all about the system of community notices, which are circulated on a clipboard from one apartment to the next. Over tea one afternoon, she went through the circulars one by one: local meetings and events; earthquake procedures; supplies which should be kept on hand for emergency use; precautions to take against possible theft over the coming New Year holiday season (an especially risky time, she said, because everyone has extra cash from their recent bonus payments). Everyone in the apartment block has to take a turn in being responsible for circulating such notices, as well as for collecting the monthly amenities fee and keeping the garbage area clean. Slightly concerned about language difficulties and procedures, I quickly worked out that with twenty-five apartments in our block, this monthly duty would only come around once every two years. Mrs Morimoto told me not to worry; she'd let me know when it was my turn and help if necessary.

She also told me that on the last Sunday morning of each month, weather permitting, a community clean-up and gardening busy bee is held around the apartment block. The next one was the coming Sunday. 'Please come and join us and introduce yourself to the other women. They would like to meet you', she said. The following Sunday morning, after we'd finished clearing and weeding, Mrs Morimoto gathered all the women neighbours around me in a semi-circle and one by one, with a certain amount of embarrassment, we introduced ourselves. Our block representative indicated, through Mrs Morimoto, which of the row of small garden plots was ours to cultivate. Three of the women shyly asked if I would help with their English conversation. Of course, I agreed and we fixed a time to meet. Later that afternoon, I dug over our small garden patch, removing stones and builder's rubble and burying kitchen scraps for compost.

Our informal, *ad hoc* English conversation group proved to be an unanticipated opportunity for sharing information and views on a range of subjects, as well as for organising outings to museums, exhibitions and the theatre. On numerous occasions, over green tea and *mochi* cakes, we talked about topics ranging from *kabuki* to contraception, marriages to meals, peacekeeping forces to probation, and schooling to shopping. My neighbours explained how the system of 'arranged' marriages had worked for them. Mrs Shiomoto laughingly described how she had rejected three or four potential partners before finally deciding whom she would marry. Mrs Sakuma said she married the first potential spouse introduced to her. His education and prospects were good and after a few meetings they decided to get married. 'It's okay', she remarked, laughing.

I hardly ever see their husbands. But then neither do my women neighbours. Their husbands typically leave any time between 7.30 and 9.30 in the morning, and don't usually arrive home until well after 9 p.m., often midnight. But a Japanese wife is still expected to welcome her husband home and have his bath ready. 'How do you stay awake, if he's so late every night?' I asked Mrs Shiomoto. 'Oh, I often sleep in the afternoon', she smiled. When the government began closing its offices on Saturday mornings, my women neighbours were generally not too happy. 'I'll just have to spend more time preparing food for him', grumbled one.

The world of my women neighbours in Moon Tree Hill is a full, friendly and close-knit one. Many of their daily activities are undertaken collectively. One day as I was cycling off to do some shopping, I noticed a small cluster of them examining the contents of assorted cardboard boxes outside our apartment block. I must have looked intrigued. 'Ah, this is the co-op', said Mrs Shiomoto, jumping up, 'I'll explain all about it to you later'. She did, and I began to learn about the variety of food co-ops delivering in the neighbourhood. Membership, orders, weekly deliveries of fresh, frozen, bottled and canned produce: it sounded very convenient, though rather too complicated for me, as a non-Japanese speaker, to participate in. But not long afterward, Mrs Yuasa invited me to simply add my requirements to her weekly order. Among many items I've bought from her co-op are soy sauce, fruit juice, pate, soy bean paste, dried bonito flakes, seaweed, ground coffee, gromwell reed tea and spaghetti.

• • •

There are very few occasions in Japan which pass without a gift being given or received. Our first direct experience was receiving a small package from a newly arrived neighbour. It was a small towel. This is the customary gift given to neighbours by a new resident as some sort of introduction and compensation for any inconvenience experienced by their moving in. We now have a fairly large collection of such gifts.

Mrs Ueda's gift-giving is becoming legendary in our family. She lives right beside us. Among other things, we've received pumpkins and potatoes from her brother-in-law's farm in Hokkaido; sprigs of peach and cherry blossom; seasonal flowers, plants and seeds; plates of *sushi*, cooked chicken and baked apples; a box of chocolates from their trip to Singapore; a special box of New Year's food; a charming silk *kimono* from her childhood; tickets for an orchid exhibition; Japanese style pickled onions; and a liquor made from plums. I quickly ran out of my supply of Australian calendars, perfume, tea towels, key rings, book marks and coasters. Whenever I take a plate of food round for her to try, she returns it with food on it for us.

There are also gifts which accompany an apology (*gomen nasai*), a sort of 'I'm sorry' or 'I beg your pardon' present. I've given one of these and I've received one. In the first case, I didn't realise that I'd actually done the correct thing until much later. About a month after we'd been living in Moon Tree Hill, Christopher was playing soccer outside with some younger boys. I'd noticed that one of the boys, aged about 11 years, had his arm in a cast in a sling. At dinner that evening, Christopher mentioned that this same boy had fallen while they were playing and hurt his other arm. 'Oh no!' I exclaimed in alarm, 'do you think he could have broken it?' I rang Mrs Shiomoto to ask if she knew. Her husband answered the telephone but I could not make myself fully understood. Shortly afterwards, our doorbell rang and it was Mrs Shiomoto. She had just contacted the boy's mother, and yes, the boy had indeed broken his other arm. 'I hope his mother realised it was an accident', I said. 'Oh yes', Mrs Shiomoto reassured me. We stood there looking at each other in disbelief. I didn't know what to say. It was nearly the New Year holidays and I imagined all the difficulties involved in caring for a child with both arms broken in separate accidents. The next day, I sent Christopher around to their apartment to offer our apologies and to give the boy a small gift of an Australian scenic calendar.

The *gomen nasai* gift that I received resulted from an incident which occurred during the monthly Sunday morning gardening busy bee. It was July, and after several months of adding kitchen scraps our garden plot was producing a few reasonable flowers and vegetables, not all of which I'd intentionally planted. In fact, one pumpkin plant was growing robustly from seeds dug in among the kitchen scraps. I'd trained it around the edge of our plot, but it grew rapidly and kept trailing beyond the limits of our small patch. It had three sizeable pumpkins maturing on the runners. Mrs Ueda complimented me on my gardening skills, but I assured her that the pumpkin plant was just a lucky accident. I was pleased with it all the same.

During the July gardening busy bee, I was chatting and working with Mrs Yuasa, weeding around the back of the apartment block. Sweating in the heat, we gradually worked our way around to join the others at the front. When Mrs Morimoto and Mrs Sakuma saw me they rushed across immediately. Mrs Morimoto explained that Mrs Sakuma had unwittingly pulled up my pumpkin plant. She reproved Mrs Sakuma, who was bowing to me and repeating *gomen nasai* and seemed close to tears. Mrs Morimoto explained that because Mrs Sakuma is a Tokyo city girl, she can't tell the difference between a weed and a vegetable. I told them not to worry, it was an accidental pumpkin anyway. Later, I retrieved the half-ripened pumpkins from the wilting runners and decided to experiment making pumpkin chutney. If it's palatable, I thought, I'll give a jar each to Mrs Sakuma and Mrs Morimoto to show them all was not lost. Later that morning, after the conclusion of the busy bee, there was a ring at our door. It was Mrs Sakuma with a *gomen nasai* gift, a caddy of English tea. The pumpkin chutney did turn out to be quite palatable, so I was able to give some to my neighbours.

We also received another sort of gift (*uji iwaii*) from a neighbour who had given birth to her third baby. Four of us had been to see her in hospital and had contributed to a present of fruit for her and a suit for her new baby. A week or so later, after leaving hospital, she gave us each a return gift of a towel to thank us for our congratulations.

When our neighbours, the Shiomoto family, were about to be transferred, I invited them round for a farewell meal. Anticipating her husband's transfer, Mrs Shiomoto had been quite prepared not to accompany him, preferring to remain in the Tokyo area with her two young sons, who were now settled in the local school, while her husband accepted the promotion and moved to a regional centre. To her surprise and delight, it happened that he was transferred to her home town, where her parents still lived. So they were going together. To our surprise that evening, *they* gave *us* farewell gifts of a Kyushu ceramic tea-set, carefully wrapped in straw in a neat wooden box, a potted plant and a bottle of *sake*. Overwhelmed, we thanked them profusely and added, 'But you're the ones who are leaving!'

During the winter and summer gift-giving seasons, department stores set aside special display areas where customers can order from a vast selection of boxed produce. Gifts are then sent directly from the store to friends, colleagues, relations or whomever. We've also received gifts of this sort. One day in December, we received a large carton of the most enormous and delicious red apples we've ever tasted. This was sent to us from a family in Iwate whom Alison had visited twice on a homestay arrangement. Receiving the other gift was a little more complicated. One of Dennis' colleagues had told him he wanted to send us a fresh salmon as a winter gift. I was intrigued as to how this salmon would be delivered. The colleague rang and told us that his wife had ordered it that day and we should expect it in the next day or so. It still hadn't arrived a few days later and we were due to leave for a weekend in Kyoto. The thought of this salmon rotting in some confined place was beginning to bother me. I urged Dennis to let his colleague know that we hadn't received the gift yet and, as we left for Kyoto, I mentioned to Mrs Ueda next door the possibility of a salmon being delivered while we were away. If it arrived, could she possibly retrieve it from our doorstep and dispose of it if necessary? She understood and would deal with it accordingly. The day after we returned, she rushed around to explain what had happened. Apparently, the salmon had been delivered the day after it had been ordered, but because no one was home, the delivery man had put it in the electrical service cupboard in the apartment block stairwell and not left a note on our door. When Mrs Ueda realised what had happened, she rang the delivery company and told them to remove the offending fish and deliver a replacement, which they did. The large fresh salmon arrived soon after in a styrofoam box filled with ice and decorated with bamboo leaves. It was delicious.

• • •

I never expected living in the greater Tokyo area to involve such cosiness and intimacy as we have experienced. Most neighbourhoods are localised urban villages, characterised by a narrow, lively shopping street. In Moon Tree Hill, our shopping street is about five minutes away by bicycle. It's at its busiest in the late part of the afternoon, when most Japanese housewives are doing their daily shopping. The shops all seem to be operated as family concerns. There are separate meat shops selling chicken, pork and beef; a fish shop, with a cheerful owner who greets shoppers and encourages them to buy from his varied selection of seafood; a *tôfu* shop, where the family makes and sells various types of soy bean curd; and several fruit and vegetable markets. I think every Japanese housewife cycles or walks home each day with a giant white radish (*daikon*) and a bunch of large green spring onions (*negi*). In one shop, which fronts directly onto the street, two or three old people sit every day, skinning onions with an air pressure hose.

Among the other small establishments in the street are stationers, florists, hardware and crockery shops, cleaners, bakers, barbers, clothiers, noodle and *sushi* bars, as well as a variety of restaurants. From some shops, you can buy take-away *yakitori*, bean cakes or assorted *tempura*. If you want to buy alcohol after the liquor shop has closed, machines outside dispense cans of beer and bottles of *sake* or whisky. The same is true at the rice and cereal shop —

a coin-operated machine in the street outside stocks 1.5 kilogram bags of rice.

The neighbourhood bathhouse is situated in the central part of the shopping street and is well patronised by people of all ages. It's common in the early evening to see casually dressed locals strolling to or from the bathhouse carrying a basket of bathing necessities.

It's rare to have a quiet day at home in Moon Tree Hill. When I do find myself happily at home for a whole day, the noises and interruptions of the neighbourhood are constant. Apart from the more usual sounds of raucous ravens and children playing, the musical garbage truck with the white-gloved garbage collectors passes daily. Assorted trucks and vans with loudspeakers announce the sale of baked goods, groceries, fruit and vegetables, laundry poles and kerosene. And in winter, a man sells sweet potatoes baked in a wood-burning oven on the back of his truck. The smell and taste are delicious, but his wailed announcement really hurts the ears.

Then there are the various door-to-door salespersons, most of whom I think are trying to sell real estate, although I think others want to sign up customers for newspaper and magazine deliveries or music lessons. Occasionally, women seeking to gain converts to one faith or another ring at the door. I must admit I was surprised to find Japanese Jehovah's Witnesses on our doorstep one day. The sight of a foreigner is usually enough to send even the most determined sales-person or 'God-botherer' politely and quickly on their way.

Another time, it wasn't clear to me what the man at the door with the receipt book actually wanted. I did what I usually do in such situations — rang my neighbour's doorbell to ask for help. It turned out the man was collecting a licence fee for a particular TV channel which we in fact got. While my neighbour was clarifying the situation with the licence fee collector, another neighbour came past. She joined the discussion, none of which I could understand. Eventually, the licence fee collector bowed several times, excused himself, bade us farewell and moved on. It transpired that my two neighbours had successfully convinced him that, as non-Japanese speakers, we should not have to pay for a TV channel which we could not understand, even if we did watch it occasionally!

Time has flown since we moved to Moon Tree Hill. Our neighbours have been generous to the extreme and have taught us a lot about living here. We have observed each other's comings and goings, chatted, laughed and cried together. Mrs Ueda jokingly told me not long ago that they were cautioned about living next door to *gaijin* when they moved in. A sort of warning to be prepared for anything those funny, fascinating foreigners, especially Australian ones, might do. But just as the novelty of having us in the neighbourhood is wearing off, we'll be sadly leaving. Will living back in Australia ever be the same after living in Moon Tree Hill?

Hachijo: A Little Piece of Australia

Frank Foley

I t all started harmlessly enough. It was August 1990. We were at the home of my fiancee's uncle on Hachijo Island for a feast of *sashimi* and other seafood delights caught by our host the day before. My fiancee's cousin and her husband, a native of Toyama prefecture, joined us. The pleasantries were predictable. Our host, Hayashi, asked me about my job; had I been back to Australia recently? He asked his nephew-in-law about Toyama, observing that between them they represented the western and eastern extremes of the country. We complimented him on his beautiful house: a picture-perfect large Japanese style house built by his father just before he retired, handing over the family construction company to Hayashi.

Then it started. We had just finished the sixth bottle of beer on this hot August night when I saw Hayashi nod subtly to his wife. 'No, no', she motioned with her eyes, 'not that, not the ...'. Shaking her head she disappeared into the kitchen, returning soon with a large brown, unopened bottle. A telepathic message zapped between my fiancee, Midori, and her cousin: 'There goes tomorrow!'.

'This is 25% proof *imo-jôchû*', explained Hayashi, 'we drink it straight, but of course if you can't handle it ...'. The challenge to the foreigner and the mainlander was clear.

The first few glasses went down easily enough, and the conversation flowed. We talked about the usual things: politics, sport, religion, fishing, wives, children. After about the fourth glass I began to have that 'Boy-my-Japanese-is-great-I-can-talk-just-like-a-native' feeling that I used to get at university parties as an exchange student. Long-forgotten vocabulary poured out as I tackled the most difficult of concepts and attempted the finest syntactical distinctions. I even found myself tracing out *kanji* on the palm of my hand and in mid air to punctuate my colourful explanations, and sucking air through my teeth just like the natives do. I think I climaxed somewhere around the tenth glass (just before I lost my memory) when, for a brief moment, I sensed that I was speaking the best Japanese in the room. Or, more precisely, that I was the only person who was understood by all. Not because I was any less drunk, but because I was the only one speaking anything that resembled standard Japanese. The more Hayashi and the nephew-in-law drank, the thicker their respective dialects became. I wasn't so much an interpreter as a decoder of Hachijo-*ben* for the Toyamans, and vice-versa.

Midori disputed this. She claimed we were all just plain drunk and not communicating at all. Her evidence for this was that we were all talking, mostly simultaneously, about completely different subjects, and were simply repeating the same thing over and over again, having long lost the ability to compose an original thought.

• • •

I woke the next morning and made a mental note in what was left of my brain never to drink *imo-jôchû* with a local again. Then I started to think about the positive side of the encounter. My overriding thought was how comfortable I felt on Hachijo. Until then Japan for me had been the concrete and hustle of Tokyo: exorbitant rents for cramped accommodation; long queues and waiting lists; constant noise. Then it clicked: Hachijo had all the 'Australian positives' that Tokyo lacked — the informality, the scenery, the space. As I lay in my *futon* (absolutely incapable of moving anything except for my eyelids and a few vital organs), I got to thinking about other similarities between Hachijo and Australia.

Despite being only 300 kilometres south of Tokyo (with approximately the same geographical coordinates as Adelaide), Hachijo has a sub-tropical climate more akin to my hometown, Brisbane. This is due to the effect of the *Kuroshio* (Black Current) which flows up from the South Pacific. The vegetation too is sub-tropical, which has fostered healthy exports of freesia, hibiscus and ornamental palms to a ready market in Tokyo. Tourism has become increasingly important: in tough economic times many young sun-lovers opt for Hachijo rather than more expensive overseas destinations.

But more striking is the similarity in the histories of Hachijo and Australia, for both served as places of exile. During the Tokugawa period (1600 to 1868) Hachijo was an exile for political prisoners known as *runin*. One legacy of this period are the distinctive *tamaishigaki* walls, built from bowling ball size boulders carried up by the *runin* from the sea. Another is that dreadful *imo-jôchû* with which Hayashi had tried to poison me. Many of the *runin* were intellectuals who contributed greatly to the culture of the island, one of the most famous being Kondo Tomizo, who compiled a multi-volume history of Hachijo during his incarceration. So taken was he by the beauty of the island that even after he was freed he chose to stay on Hachijo, where he was buried at the ripe old age of 80.

But the *runin* were only adding to an already rich cultural heritage. It is said that the reason the Tokugawa government opted to administer Hachijo directly, instead of through the more arm's-length Han-style administration, was to have access to the beautiful *kihachijo* weaving. A *kimono* woven from the distinctive yellow, brown and black patterns of *kihachijo* silk sells today for several thousand dollars.

A few hours of lying there thinking about all this and I was ready to get up. (I was also hungry and at least one other basic instinct need appeasing.) We were staying at Midori's grandmother's house, which until the previous year had been a *minshuku* lodge. I made my way from the sleeping quarters up a short hill to the main house to find O-Bâ-chan herself in one of the large *tatami* rooms making alterations to a *kihachijo kimono*.

'I made this originally for Midori's uncle', she said. 'He was from Tokyo, you know. He graduated from Tokyo University and could have taught anywhere, but he loved Hachijo so much he moved here to teach at our high school. We can go and visit his grave later on, if you like. It's just next to O-Jii-chan's (her husband's).'

'Stand up and turn around', she said as she pulled a tape measure from her pocket and started measuring across my shoulders.

In the plane back to Tokyo I babbled on to my fiancee about how Hachijo had completely changed my perception of Japan. A sub-tropical refuge just fifty minutes by plane from Tokyo. I couldn't believe it. 'Oh how I'd love to return the favour and show my Hachijo relatives the splendours of Australia. But how could we persuade them all to come down. They'd have to have one hell of a reason.'

Half asleep, Midori mumbled, 'Well, we could have the wedding in Australia'.

• • •

Thanks to a lot of help from siblings and friends in Australia, preparations for the wedding went very smoothly.

All the excitement was on Hachijo Island as fifteen relatives prepared for their adventure. There were passports and visas to be organised, tickets to be purchased and, of course, souvenir lists to be compiled. Then there was the itinerary. They were quite excited by this stage and had lots of ideas about where they wanted to visit. One itinerary had them doing Kakadu National Park, Adelaide and Perth in two days. Another, a six-day tour around the country, had them white-water rafting on the Tully River just as my wife and I would be cutting the cake. 'But what about the wedding?', we reminded them. 'Oh yeah. I don't suppose you could shift it to the Tuesday, could you?', someone asked hopefully.

The wedding in Brisbane went without a hitch. I stumbled over some of the words but Midori was fine. The reception was a showcase of international talent. A musician friend of mine sang an improvised version of Joe Jackson's 'Is She Really Going Out With Him?'; one of Midori's uncles sang a traditional folk song from Hachijo; and Midori accompanied her mother on the piano in a rendition of 'An Irish Lullaby', which brought a tear to my own mother's eye.

Then the post-wedding tour commenced. In Sydney, having 'done' the harbour, they launched into a shopping frenzy. My wife advised me to stand back until they had had their fill, assuring me that once it was out of their system that would be the end of it for the trip. Then it was on to Melbourne, where we were greeted by a good friend who had organised two days of fun and culture for the Japanese party. After a brief rest, he whisked us off to see the fairy penguins on Port Phillip Island. Even though we arrived well before sunset, the observation stands were already quite full. 'Pity', I thought, 'I would like to have got O-Bâ-chan a seat up front'. Excitement grew as progress reports came in over the loudspeaker. I explained to O-Bâ-chan that the fairy penguins were just a little way out and were expected any minute. I could see she was impressed when I added that they had been out for up to three days feeding and fetching food for their young, which were hidden in the dunes behind us.

'And here they come', went the announcement, bringing the crowd to its feet. 'But they're so small', whispered O-Bâ-chan, clearly moved that these little animals would struggle in the high seas for days on end just to feed their young. She actually shed a tear for the tiny battlers as they scurried past the tourists to the dunes and their young beyond.

On day two, my friend whisked us off to ride the Puffing Billy through the Dandenongs in the morning, and to a hearty country lunch at a sheep station. That afternoon we visited a wildlife reserve on the road back to Melbourne, to give our Japanese visitors first-hand exposure to some Australian flora and fauna. No one will ever forget the sight of O-Bâ-chan being followed around the park by an inquisitive emu, which stopped each time she halted to admire the flowers.

Their last night in Australia was spent at a beautiful beach-side seafood restaurant facing due west over the expanse of Port Phillip Bay. The Hachijoans were beside themselves with the beautiful seafood, and a couple, I think, were just a little bit homesick as they looked out over the water. As long as I live I will never forget the image of O-Bâ-chan across the table wearing top-of-the-range Raybans borrowed from a grandchild, and looking out at the setting sun as she wondered, I'm sure, how the fairy penguins were faring tonight.

· · ·

On our last trip to Hachijo, just before *O-bon* this year, I drove O-Bâ-chan over to her husband's grave on one of her regular visits. As I burned some incense and poured water wherever she told me to, I asked whether I could be buried there too. She said yes.

Sensô Memories

Josie Gibson

When I remember Mr Ishii, I feel only sadness. It's years ago now, but I can still see his lined face with its burden of private pain, which he tried to shake off but probably took to his grave. For a fleeting moment I came close to seeing his demons, but as often happens, the moment passed, and he retreated once more behind his wall of money and influence.

The day I first met Mina and Mr Ishii, Sapporo had just shaken off the sludge and rain of early spring for the luminescence of summer greenery. The old men and their wives had disrobed the parks and gardens, the trees and shrubs surviving the past winter trussed like bon-bons in cones of woven straw. For weeks now around Tokyo they had been out viewing the cherry blossoms and swilling beer, but this far north the delicate pink blooms hadn't yet appeared.

In this place southerners still refer to disparagingly as the frontier, the wind can blow straight off Siberia, and in the impatience of spring it seems to take eons to massage life into the city after months of snow-laden semi-paralysis. Without that spectacular white cover, Sapporo looks like any other city in northern Japan; grey tenements jostling for space, the odd multi-storey, the occasional vegetable patch, and rows of houses with funny sloping roofs, now vaguely out of place with nothing to slough off. Still, it's the sort of place one quickly grows to love, if one is possessed of that frontier spirit and admires the no-nonsense approach of its inhabitants, who operate unhampered by many of the tedious traditions of the south. And then there are the mountains, throwing their protective ring around Sapporo, their presence both picturesque and reassuring.

But that particular spring day when Kimiko took me to meet Mr Ishii, the streets of the city were languid with warmth. I was fuelled by the approaching summer and irritated that Kimiko had to come along at all. She was attired in her best *kimono* of sombre greys and blues, which slowed down our progress somewhat, but in these days of dying traditions would serve to impress. I suspect she also wanted to view this rich man who was commandeering we Australian students for the weekend. She might too have been picturing her weatherbeaten home with its primitive bathroom against his money and private plane and felt a bit wanting.

As usual, we took the subway with its Strauss waltzes and eat-off-the-floor cleanliness into Odori Park, which slices right through most of the city centre. The subway cars were redolent with sweaty, exuberant students returning from Saturday classes, the boys in their stiff Prussian-style uniforms, many of the young girls in the sailor suits of junior high school. Probably more than a few of them were heading to another session at cram school.

Mr Ishii didn't disappoint the myth we'd been busy building since receiving a summons to stay. Like a destroyer, a black Lincoln Continental swept in from out of nowhere, dwarfing the streets and the surrounding traffic. Mr Ishii leapt from its depths and proceeded with great energy to rush around bowing and shaking hands. In his wake followed the wraith-like Mina, a beautiful Filipina trainee who was spending a year in Sapporo learning the ropes at a local television station. We were, as it turned out, being shanghaied to keep her company for the weekend.

Looking back, Mina never did tell us much about Mr Ishii, almost as if she'd been sworn to secrecy at some point long ago. All she would let on was that her family back in Quezon City were 'friends' of the Ishiis. But even if she had attempted some introduction in those first few hours, we were too busy gawking at the interior of the Ishii mansion to pay much attention. The Lincoln had disgorged us outside a large house not far from the Toyohira River in eastern Sapporo. Typically, the outside gave away few clues; but the rather unprepossessing concrete exterior gave way to an opulence inside that was overwhelming. Except for the *tatami* in the Japanese-style room and heated tiles in the cavernous bathroom, the house had carpet throughout, deep enough to lose a small dog in. Footsteps transformed into gentle shush-shushing, giving the house a subdued air. It was hard to imagine children running carefree along that corridor. In months of being feted by various city fathers, we hadn't come across anything so ostentatiously luxurious. We look back now and laugh at our bemused embarrassment in tackling the bathroom and toilet, where hi-tech equipment carried a certain amount of peril for the uninitiated.

The Ishiis were collectors: Momoyama-period lacquered lunch boxes, Zen Buddhist alms bowls, late Edo sea-chests, exquisite scrolls and *netsuke* of all descriptions. There was also the odd piece from the Philippines. As the weekend progressed, Mr Ishii's obsession with the Philippines and its residents became clear.

A strong, stocky man with sharp eyes, he was accustomed to getting his own way. He instructed us to call him Papa Ishii, as Mina did, and insisted on speaking in halting but determined English when we were quite capable of understanding his Japanese. This dominance would no doubt have come in handy in raking together his empire, but I wondered about his wife: she glided around in her expensive clothes and said little except to inquire politically about our wants and needs. Her mien of sadness could not be concealed by 'Shiseido'. There was no mention of any children, but in my inquiries afterwards I learned there had been an only child, a son who had died quite young in a car crash.

I also found that like most Japanese men of his age, Mr Ishii had fought in the war. It was still a rather sensitive subject for many older Japanese, I had discovered, so I had to abate my curiosity for first-hand accounts of Japan's side of the war, disappointing because I had wanted to balance my father's experience in Borneo.

Mr Ishii did give the war passing mention during the weekend to explain his interest in the Philippines. But while he said little else, I guessed that somehow, forty years later, the war was not over for Mr Ishii. It had guided his career and influenced his life, and now its black memories hung over his twilight years. Remorse hung about him like an albatross. The Philippines had emerged from the war devastated, with a death toll of around one million, one of them Mr Ishii's only brother. He seemed to imply it was just punishment for the fighting — whatever he'd done — on Philippine soil all those years ago.

I learned all this later, of course, from someone else. It made me forgive Mr Ishii his aggression and see that empty, opulent house in a new light. As it was explained to me, Mr Ishii had returned to the destruction of postwar Japan and set about making his fortune in construction and related industries. From fairly humble beginnings, he became a millionaire. But he could not forget the war, and continued to return to the Philippines as if summoned there by the spirit of his dead brother. He built factories and roads and employed countless Philippine workers. He also brought young Philippine men and women to Japan in an effort to give them a better start in life. Mina was not the first trainee to be hosted by the Ishiis, but she was to be the last.

There were signs that weekend that he was preparing to let go, to succumb to the demons plaguing him. Much of the time he threw into arranging activities for us, showering us with expensive gifts. But there were moments when the beefy shoulders sagged and his eyes took on a tiredness not explained by age. Mina herself seemed a bit cowed by him, and not without her own air of melancholy. One got the impression it hadn't been her wish to leave her family for a year and spend it in this barren house. Later, she seemed to wilt a bit more each time we saw her, and a short time before she returned to Quezon City she contracted tuberculosis. She recovered, of course, but we felt it was due to living in that unhappy house under its shadow of the past.

It was a strange, surreal weekend. Nothing was too much trouble for Mr Ishii, but his kindness was remote and automatic and didn't really touch us.

• • •

There was really only one time I came close to seeing Mr Ishii without his armour. It was probably eighteen months later, and I was making a return visit to Sapporo. The city was already buried under deep snow and I found it difficult to retrace the route to the Ishii mansion in that unfamiliar part of town. Steam rose off the Toyohira River and the scraping of snow shovels echoed through the narrow streets.

Once again, it was a Saturday. I rang the bell. Nothing happened for a while, then the intercom at the gate crackled and I heard his voice bark. I had thought he might not remember me, but Mr Ishii, I know now, never forgot anything. He carried memories around like a cross, rarely examining them individually but always straining under their weight. I could see he had been sitting in the semi-darkened living room, nursing a glass. There was no sign of Mrs Ishii and I gathered she had gone to Tokyo to escape the cold.

Mr Ishii was overwhelmed I should come to visit him after all this time and immediately began organising on my behalf, the way an old person would. Funny that I had never thought of him as old before then; but, of course, he must have been getting on. I gently told him my itinerary had been set. I had stopped by to pay my respects, and to thank him for his generosity the year before. He accepted all this with gruff resignation, but insisted on arranging a gift for me. By phone he summoned a jeweller and, over my protestations, commanded me to wait. Before long the buzzer at the gate announced the jeweller's arrival. In he scurried with a large briefcase, which Mr Ishii instructed him to open before me. It was embarrassing, yet thrilling, to be the focus of such attention. The briefcase was full of watches, expensive watches, mostly Japanese, but a few of European make. I was heady with the choices. Pick one, Mr Ishii ordered. But I couldn't; it was beyond me. Instead, Mr Ishii chose for me, one with two types of gold and silver and a delicate bracelet band. I accepted with numb gratitude, and put it on. That action seemed to bring alive, for a brief moment, some sort of spark in Mr Ishii.

When I left he embraced me at the *genkan*. I was shocked at such an expansive show of emotion by a Japanese. Somehow I knew, though, and he knew too, that we would never meet again.

A few months later, Mr Ishii was dead. I received a terse note from Mrs Ishii, postmarked Tokyo. I would never know if he'd finally made his peace with the war.

Fifteen years later the watch still works.

Drawing the Line

Geoff Bolton

On returning to Japan to marry, Mr Kato became Mr Ando.

The couple came back from their honeymoon in Hawaii, back to his work, Mr and Mrs Ando; and the very next month he'd refused a promotion. Promotion to deputy section chief — *kachô-dairi* — of the hides business: an important post within this branch of the Company.

Yet Kato–Ando had declined to accept it, expressing sincere gratitude, of course, for his selection but declining it, firmly and repeatedly.

Barry Nolan thinks on these matters as he slits the paper wrapping from a small carton of name cards: new cards for a new name. He opens the carton and checks the top card, turning it over; English on one side, Japanese characters on the other; Ando Kyusaku, they announce. Barry wonders whether Ando Kyusaku has much of a future now, with the Company.

He drops the carton of cards into his out-tray. From his desk, these will find their way to the desk of Kyu Kato-become-Ando; ordering of stationery is one of the small duties which Barry has accumulated in his years at this office.

It is five p.m. on a Friday, drinking time, and tomorrow is the industry picnic day. He sighs; the Company holds this picnic jointly with the other trading houses involved in the business. Once each year, their commercial rivalries are put aside — or channelled into sporting competition. Barry Nolan groans at the prospect, but cannot avoid it; a duty. All Company staff are expected to attend, to take part with their families and friends. He has been able to shuffle his access weekend so Kelly can come; his daughter is fourteen. He'll be busy on the day, but it will make a change for her. She'll enjoy it, anyhow.

· · ·

This year the weather has been kind, not sunny, and low-moving clouds warn of its uncertainty; but the day is warm, and a cooling breeze comforts the first families to arrive, emerging sweaty from the baking cars, unbending from the clammy seats. The children explode across the grass; they invade trees to heights already frightening to their mothers and dabble at the river's edge with careless feet as fathers rush to restrain them.

It is eleven-thirty; the locals begin to arrive, and unlike the Japanese already congregated into familiar groups, they strike out for vacant corners of the park, waving at recognised friends in other gatherings. 'Barry!' He squints across the grass, towards the calling of his name, and waves at a drinking friend from Marubeni. Barry Nolan struggles with a gas bottle beneath the portable barbecue — one of his duties.

Kelly is important in her father's old apron; sorting the steaks, the chops, the sausages, and slicing the onions. From a group of Nissho-Iwai people, his friend Graham approaches, an opened can of beer in each hand; Barry accepts one, and waves towards the carpark where Kyu Ando and his wife are unloading bags of ice. They smile, returning his wave.

'So, what's all this about Kyu, then?' asks Graham. 'Changes his name. Now I hear he wants to knock back a promotion? Bet they just *love* that, eh?'

'Yeah. It shook them up a bit. Didn't know *what* to make of it — even asked *me* about it, the little buggers. Hadn't a clue, of course.'

'Strange. Very, very strange; for one of them, I mean.'

'Shh, they're coming over now.'

• • •

Kneeling on their spread rug, watchful for ants or something worse, Mrs Komata and Mrs Homma are friends. Not close friends — merely playing golf and tennis each week — but grateful for each other on an occasion like this. Mrs Homma fends flies from her face with a bamboo fan as they silently watch the arrival of the newly married couple; they see Ando Kyusaku accept a can of beer from one of the locals, he quaffs it directly. Mrs Komata shakes her head and sips neatly at a paper cup; Mrs Homma's mouth is a taut line of disapproval. She offers her companion a plastic dish of pickles and dried fish, and a small wooden fork. Mrs Komata smiles, gesturing towards the open ground where Mrs Homma's husband, the branch manager, stands ready to organise the day's first sporting events. Their smiles are matched in both timing and restraint.

Across the grass, children churn about Mr Homma; first a three-legged race. He blows a whistle in short warnings as the entrants form a ragged line; comic in his golf shirt, a much-stained fishing cap, shorts and knee-socks. Some local parents help to organise the start, and a fierce blast from his whistle starts the race. The event is interrupted: little Yamada Tanjuro must be rescued from the river, canoe-capsized in his latest flirtation with drowning. His mother seems unable to choose her emotion — relief at his deliverance, or remorse at the interruption of the day's program; she will spend the rest of this day bowing to any who might have been inconvenienced; but her young Tanjuro is already in dry clothes, urging her towards the next event — a tug-of-war.

A column of smoke climbs into the sky from the barbecue area; arrays of meat are ruined to varying degrees by the local husbands, cherishing their custom of cooking. Their wives resignedly give out paper plates, plastic cutlery, and other implements of doubtful aid in the conquest of food. Behind the barbecue, Ando seems affected by its smoke — or is he getting drunk? His face is very red. Near him, Barry calls out to Kelly as she throws herself into the next cluster of bodies heaving at a weighty rope; Homma, mock-solemn, holds his fan above the centre, over a fluttering red ribbon. One burst from his whistle collapses this contest into a heap of bodies, with protests, tears and laughter.

Kyu Ando stumbles against Barry. 'Your daughter, Barry-san *ne*? So quickly growing up?'

Barry nods. He is proud of her, and of what she is becoming. He scoops up two fresh cans of beer. 'Ready for another, Kyu old mate?'

Ando shakes his head, grinning, He pats the side of his face. '*Maa*, Barry, too much. Already over exceeding quota, *ne*?' They laugh together.

'Glad you could come along, Kyu. You and the wife. It's a nice day too. For everyone here, I reckon.'

'*Sô ne*, thank you so much. For inviting us. Even if I have some, ah, problem with *kaisha*, with the Company, *ne*?'

Barry scratches his head. 'Look mate, it's none of my business, I know that. But the Company isn't bloody well God now, is it? I mean, well good on you I reckon — too few of you blokes seem to be willing to draw the line with them. They treat you like a whole lot of ants. Yeah, *ants*!'

He likes this simile; turning its image over in his mind.

'Like a heap of ants. That *is* what it looks like sometimes, Kyu old mate. Hope I don't seem rude, but, well, more of you blokes should stand up for yourselves. Right?'

Ando twists his head, seems perplexed. 'Ahh, thank you Barry. So thoughtful. However, not so easy for us to stay here now. Rather difficult situation, *ne*?'

'Well, you can at least — look around. Wool. You're our acknowledged expert there. Bet you could find another job here. Easy. If that's what you want, of course.'

'Ah, Barry, *too* kind, *ne*. But wool business . . . *not* so strong, I think. Very little prospect for jobs here now, I think.' Barry knows he is right, Ando really is out on a limb.

Another tug-of-war collapses in noise and complaint. Parents bustle about, organising and reshaping; short blasts from Homma's whistle bring order as the rope tautens again. Barry drains his beer, throws it towards a rubbish bin and misses. 'And another thing, Kyu old mate — y'don't mind me calling you that? I mean to say, this Kato–Ando change. Well, it takes some getting used to for me. You understand?'

'No worries, Barry mate. No worries, *ne*?' Ando grins at him.

Barry laughs, 'Seriously, but . . .'

'What?'

'Well, I mean, this name business. Anybody who knocks back a job — one they don't really want — that I can understand. But the name change. If you'd rather not tell me, say so. But I just can't put a handle on that one.'

Ando bunches tissues to wipe at his face and neck. He is silent for a little while. Then he answers Barry, in a lowered voice. 'Kato, *ne,* Kato is only a name. Rather a common name, I may say.'

He glances over his shoulder at the noise of an adult team forming at each end of the great rope; 'Also, I may say, to take name of wife's family, *ne? Not* so unusual in some of our situations. Part of marriage, ah, agreement, *ne?*'

'Part of the package, like?'

'*Sô.*' Ando giggles, smiling as he repeats the phrase. 'Part-of-the-package, *sô ne*, Barry-san. You see, if I am younger brother, and if wife's family has no sons, *ne?* Then *they* may adopt *me*. Wife's family adopts husband, so he takes their name.' He nods to affirm this, in the face of Barry's incredulous look.

'Jeezus. We live and learn. So that's why you stopped being Kato. But what about that family — your own family? The Katos. What do they think of all this?'

Ando seems to avoid this point; his wife is walking towards them across the grass. He only says, 'Not so unusual, Barry. Not so unusual'.

• • •

The great rope again swings heavily above the grass as if with its own life; adults and teenagers are drawn to clasp at its ends. It becomes its own creature, drawing at the people trapped into its tension; each pair of straining legs balanced by an opposing pair of legs, grinding for footholds in the ruptured grass. This equilibrium imparts to the rope a quivering life: the red ribbon hovers between the teams, edging left then right; but gradually, steadily, more left than right; more west than east. The eastern team fights against the rope's demand and the sun, now in their eyes. Homma, the referee, is crouched across the ribbon on the now-solid rope, as anchoring pairs of feet scour their opposing furrows — slowly forward for the eastern team, against groans and grunts. The smaller children scream as they rush to any vacant gap in the rope. Now the western team counts 'One. Two. Three. *Washoi!*' and falls backward in their final effort; both teams lie collapsed in winded, laughing heaps. Homma, ceremonious, flicks his fan open towards the western end to a chorus of merged cheers and boos. Among the sprawled bodies, the children's drink brigade dashes with beer, with lemonade.

And they are most welcome.

· · ·

Across the ground, under shading trees, Mrs Komata abandons her scorched steak: she nibbles at some home-made *onigiri* — complimenting Mrs Homma on them — the compact neatness of each strip of paper-like seaweed wrapped about a ball of rice, each with its own centre of dried fish or pickle. They do not look at, nor speak of, the Ando couple. In her role as convenor of their tennis club, Mrs Komata has decided against inviting the newcomer Mrs Ando to join. Suddenly, children — Japanese children and local children — surround them, demanding that the two women join in with the next event: a three-legged race, for wives, girlfriends, mothers. Kelly is running around the park to find Mrs Ando, to be her partner.

· · ·

'Look, you'd tell me, Kyu, if this is none of my business, right?'

Ando smiles at his companion. Sitting side by side on the grass, they watch Kelly dragging his wife towards the starting line. 'It is good, sometimes to talk, Barry-san.'

'You sure now?'

'*Hontô, yo*. Rather difficult for me to talk of these things with my Japanese, ah — friends. They may have rather rigid views on these questions, as you know.'

'Yeah, I've noticed. Well, tell me all about — if you feel okay about it', says Barry crumpling an empty can in one fist.

'*Sô, ne*. Sometimes Barry, we meet doors in our lives. Some doors are to enter — for advantage, *ne*?'

'Okay, I can see that.' Barry nods.

'But, some other doors. We may wish to close them. Better never to open them, for our own benefit, of course.'

'Of course.' They see the women and girls being aligned into pairs for the three-legged race; their ankles are bound.

'The Ando family was happy to adopt me — and I to adopt their name.'

'A nice gesture, too. For your wife, I mean.'

Ando Kyusaku shakes his head, 'Not for my wife, Barry. For me. I changed my name for myself. My own interest, *ne*?'.

For once, Barry is silent; a fresh can of beer halfway to his mouth.

'Barry-san, Barry-san, *ne*. For me it was a doorway, to escape my old past.'

'Your old past? But why?'

Ando looks around the picnic grounds, and at the groups closest to them. 'In English, you have a word — Untouchable, *ne*?'

'Untouchable? You mean like in India? The lowest classes.'

'*Sô*, exactly. But such a system. Not only India, *ne*?'

'You mean, Japan too? They have it here too? You amaze me.' Barry sits up. He wonders if Kyu is joking.

Ando looks up at the sky, still filled with rolling grey clouds; he looks again at the people closest to them, then to Barry Nolan. 'You will *never* hear of it — even many Japanese, the younger ones, are truly ignorant of it. But the others, most people, they do not wish to know. Or to admit that they know, *ne*.' He looks carefully around again, and whispers: '*Buraku*. You must tell nobody, of course. *No*-body. My family was — is — *buraku-min*'.

Ando explains the separation, the otherness, of generation after generation of those families involved in 'unclean work'; animal slaughter, tanning, many facets of the meat industry; *buraku*, the unclean community.

'You amaze me', Barry says, slowly shaking his head. 'In a modern country like that. It's almost — feudal. Bloody feudal. How do you — they — survive?'

'But we are not all poor, Barry-san', laughs Kyu. 'Our family business in Akagi — near to Osaka, *ne*? My brother — elder brother — he runs it, tanning and making leather goods. Very profitable — good business, *ne*.'

'Does the Company know?'

Ando shakes his head. 'No, not officially. After my graduation, I studied about textile science — I moved to Nagoya. So to wool, so to Aus-tralia.'

'Well, you're certainly seen as the wool expert round here.'

'So, better to stay in same area, *ne*?'

Barry sighs, rubbing at the top of his head. 'So that's why you refused the new job, the promotion. The hides section.'

'*Sô*, exactly *ne*. Too many people in that business — they might connect me, as one of the Kato family.'

After one false start, Homma is reorganising the women and girls.

'Does she know — and her family?' asks Nolan.

Ando nods. '*Sô*, she understands. That is okay — we had a "love marriage", *ne*? Not arranged by families, so her family does not know, yet.'

Barry grasps Kyu's shoulder; Kyu does not pull free from his grip. 'But when they *do*, what then? Jeez, what a business!'

'They will, they will, *ne*. Then some trouble, I guess. But by then, perhaps — well, perhaps we have some children.' He smiles. 'Security, *ne*?'

You poor buggers, you poor screwed-up buggers, thinks Barry.

They both leap to their feet at the shrieks from Homma's whistle; laughing at the sight of fourteen females, various in age and height, staggering across the grass in their awkward embraces and bound legs. They are grimly striving, and none more so than Mrs Homma and Mrs Komata, united in a neat cohesion of legs and swinging arms; well ahead of the others, until some small mistiming leaves them sprawled across the grass.

Kerry Nolan and Mrs Ando squeal as they thump over the finish line to repeated bursts from Homma's whistle. They jump in shared joy, till their still-tied legs bring them giggling to the ground. Ando and Nolan run to help, and to congratulate them.

Barry Nolan laughs, but thinks of the new name cards on his desk. Ando Kyusaku, Kyu Ando. Living on a knife-edge, in so many ways. What if her family found out soon? What if the Company knew, old Homma for instance? Living on a knife-edge, yet — for today, at least — they are living. He thinks to send Kelly for some beer, but she is already returning to where they are resting on the grass. Without asking or being asked, she brings four cans dripping from the ice. Her father grins as she expertly opens them: One. Two. Three. Four.

Yurakucho

Craig J. Dickson

I only saw him once.

It was one of those brutally hot afternoons for which the Tokyo summer is roundly infamous. Thirty-four degrees, seventy-two per cent humidity and the stone and reflecting glass offering no respite.

I cut out of the office early. The market had been shut an hour already and the prospect of a long, cold Asahi Dry was hugely to be preferred to another phone call. So I shot the gap along with the throng of like-minded returnees.

Head down against the heat, I first saw him when I glanced up to check a step. It was the hat that caught my eye. One of those upside down, woven straw, bowl-like things. It seemed frozen in front of me, like a raft becalmed in the torrent of humanity raging around him.

In fact, it was that apparent immobility that drew me to him. I moved closer and it was only when I saw his feet that I realised he was actually moving. Not standing silent in supplication, but moving, ever so slowly. It was more of a shuffle really, with each foot deliberately placed just in front of the other, before pausing. Heel-to-toe and stop; heel-to-toe and stop. You could have set your watch by him.

This was the closest I had ever been to an *o-bôsan*. Sure, everyone's been out to the temple to buy lucky arrows at New Year. But here he was in the middle of town; a monk on the factory floor almost.

He appeared to shimmer in the afternoon haze. His under-*kimono* was a brilliant white — unlined, and not rumpled by the heat. And on his feet were equally dazzling *tabi*. Even the carefully darned patches on his rust-coloured robe paid no attention to the humidity. He looked impeccably ironed, as he painfully and slowly heel-and-toed his way around the corner.

Fascinated, I stopped in the shadows of the subway entrance to survey him more closely. I could not see his face under the basket that framed his head, although the wooden beads slung low around his neck were plain. But it was the way he carried his arms, partly out, that was the most intriguing. In his right hand he held, upturned, a small wooden bowl. A petitioner's catch-all. And in his left, he bore a small bell — the source of the sound which had made me look up in the first place, so unusual was its jingling amongst the clamour of the traffic and the crowds hustling towards the subway.

I watched his languid progress a while longer. Heel-to-toe and stop, tinkle on the bell; heel-to-toe and stop, tinkle. And all the time the bowl held out in appeal. An ethereal accomplishment in the face of the onrushing populace surrounding him. It was quite unlike the alms collection of the black-frocked priests I was used to. The only similarity was in the mumbled platitudes of the priests, for I finally realised that my *o-bôsan* was also conversing under his breath. Quite inaudibly, chanting to himself a meditative sutra as he wound his way across the flagstones.

But in all the time I watched him, only once did any sound emanate from the collection bowl. For all the hundreds that brushed past this quiet monk, but a single hunched figure stopped to contribute. Among a thousand shoppers, only one old woman found the time to give. And, in fact, her gnarled fingers almost gave her away as well. Jostled by the crowds, she fumbled for the coins before finally, with a hint of veneration, she managed to bestow her offering and was moved on.

His demeanour never changed — heel-to-toe and stop, tinkle; heel-to-toe and stop, tinkle. However, I think I did discern a slight pause and a nearly imperceptible bow of the head when the old woman's contribution clunked in to the bowl. It seemed a bow of thanks, although delivered as if in embarrassment. And I began to wonder if this priest of mine really was a religious anachronism in this glass and marble city. Or was he merely prospecting on the wrong street corner?

Soon the humidity forced me also down to the sanctuary of the air-conditioned platform. I left him to his invocation — a wistful island in a tide of polyester suits.

Or so I thought. For the bell and his appeal came with me. Even over the roar of the oncoming train, I could still hear the tinkle of his bell faintly echoing down the crowded stairways.

But no one else seemed to notice.

Of Motorcycles and Hospitals

Mark Thackray

A nybody who has ever thrown their leg over a motorcycle will tell you what fun they are. Whether you're sitting high in the saddle, cruising along coastal highways, or leaning low into corners on windy mountain roads, riding a motorcycle draws you into the scenery like a car can never hope to. Even wearing a helmet, you see the beauty of the countryside without the frame of a windscreen. You're not viewing a picture from behind a pane of glass; you're right out there interacting with it.

Japan is a beautiful country, and it seems a shame not to get in amongst it as you travel around. Riding a motorcycle is exciting, but like all thrills it carries with it a certain amount of danger. My good friend was always telling me: 'Two-wheelers eventually fall over'. And you know what? He was right.

Riding a motorcycle makes a lot of sense in a country where the petrol prices are more than double those in Australia. Maybe that's why service station attendants run out to greet you when you arrive. They were always happy to see me in my car that cost over $100 to fill. Mind you, they were just as enthusiastic when I pulled in on my motorcycle, which uses only about $12 a tank and takes me a lot further. Whenever I can, I slip on my riding gear and head for the mountains.

The tendency for Japanese to do things in groups extends to riding motorcycles. Except in the winter, when it is just *too* invigorating, gangs of riders head off (in flying formation) on pre-arranged tours. Hot springs, fun parks and other tourist attractions are popular destinations. I was intrigued, so I joined a group to cross the Island of Honshu from the Sea of Japan to the Pacific Ocean and back again in one long, wonderful, tiring day. The scenery, and what I found to be most surprising — the sense of belonging — were well worth the saddle sores. That trip was the closest I've come to feeling Japanese, yet walking like John Wayne.

Probably 99 per cent of motorcycles in Japan are made here. Which isn't surprising in a country that makes the finest, most reliable bikes in the world. My love affair with Italian bikes ended after having to push one up more hills than I care to remember. Perhaps national temperament somehow finds expression in a country's motorcycles: powerful Americans, stalwart Brits, fiery Italians, serious Germans, and, well, hard-working Japanese. After riding a Japanese bike it's easy to take reliability for granted.

It's expensive to obtain a car licence in Japan — around $3,000 in the big cities. And before you're allowed to buy a car you have to prove that you have somewhere to park it. Japan's cities are congested, like all modern cities, with cars, buses and stressed-out people. Motorcycles make commuting and parking far easier. But getting a motorcycle licence also requires determination. To limit the number of big motorcycles on the road, the government demands that prospective riders be able to lift the bike they intend to ride! And bikers have to ride very slowly on a 35 mm wide strip for 10 metres and not even *appear* to lose their balance. Needless to say, people riding 1000 cc motorcycles are respected by those on lesser bikes.

The Japanese drive on the left, so that didn't require any adjustment for me, but I was taken aback by the patronisingly low national speed limits: 50 kilometres per hour on country highways and 80 on the freeways. Nearly every intersection in Japan has a large convex mirror situated so that you can see vehicles coming from all directions. A very civilised idea; just like the common practice of dimming headlights at traffic lights to avoid annoying the people in front. And what's the blood alcohol limit? My Japanese friends couldn't understand the question; if you drink *any* alcohol you're not allowed on the road in Japan.

With all this safety on Japan's roads, why are so many people killed in accidents? The answer is pure, unadulterated stupidity: there's as much of it in Japan as anywhere else, and more cars and narrower roads make it a lot easier to hit somebody. Poorly enforced seat belt laws, too, which only apply to passengers in the front, mean that crashes turn into tragedies. The Highway Police have the right idea, even if it seems a bit extreme: they wear crash helmets inside their patrol cars.

The laws of physics, on the other hand, *are* universally obeyed. A car cut in front of me on the highway several months ago, leaving me no choice but to hit it. After rolling towards eternity, sky-ground-sky-ground-sky, I came to rest with one very badly broken leg. The ambulance people picked up the man who fell to earth and taught me a word I was to hear over and over in the ensuing months: *gaman* ('soldier on', 'patience' or 'grit'). When I asked for an injection for the pain the ambulance man responded with that one word.

I was wheeled into the emergency room where they took off my leather jacket and the denim jacket I had been wearing underneath. The doctor took one look at my leg and said in faltering English, 'Must cut it off'. The words stung. I was in shock. I knew my leg was in bad shape, but surely it wasn't irreparable. New thoughts occurred to me as quickly as they could replace the old. This was Japan. It was a country hospital. I envisioned myself hobbling around on a wooden leg for the rest of my life. 'NOOOO-ooohh', I screamed.

As it turned out, they were referring to my pants. It wasn't possible to take them off my twisted leg. When I realised the misunderstanding, I laughed at what was undoubtedly the funniest joke in the world.

Japanese hospitals, I've since found out, are top notch. This is much to my relief, as I've had a couple of operations on my leg and a blood transfusion, which means that I have some Japanese blood in me! I have been institutionalised for over three months now. In fact, I'm writing this story while sitting on my bed in hospital — utilising my time in Japan's Club Med(ical) as best I can. Here, patients are treated to unlimited quantities of *bancha* tea, which is a lovely touch of hospitality. Unfortunately, like all hospices, this one dishes out fairly bland food. I enjoyed Japanese food before I was admitted, but now I'm not so sure. The other week I was served up whale, which was the first time I'd tucked into the sea mammal. *How was it*? Bland, of course.

There have been some funny moments, like when a nurse first gave me a thermometer and I put it under my tongue. She couldn't believe it: under the arm is the usual position in Japan. It was also amusing when the oxygen mask refused to fit over my foreign nose. And special crutches had to be ordered from Britain because I was too big for what they had in stock.

When I say I'm in pain the nurses will ask, '*Gaman dekiru*?' (Can you soldier on?). If I say no, they will take my temperature and maybe my blood pressure and tell me that it's okay and then leave. Nevertheless, I sometimes say, 'But haven't you forgotten something? What about the pain?'. I'm sure they exist, it's just that I've yet to see an oral painkiller, even aspirin, in a Japanese hospital. Apparently tablets with a codeine content of more than one per cent aren't sold in Japan. In theory, pharmaceutical companies could get around this by making huge tablets, but they don't. Thankfully, my parents sent me some *sub rosa* from Australia. I don't think I'm a drug fiend, but isn't that what they all say. (Just joking!)

If I persist about the pain, the nurses will give me a suppository, but in asking for one I feel like I'm letting the side down. I'm much happier now that I have my own stash, throwing *gaman* to the wind and still appearing to be a team player.

While in hospital, I've had much time to ponder the way different cultures view pain, and here's what I think: The Western, Christian ideal is to avoid pain at all costs. Very deep in our psyche, we believe we simply shouldn't be suffering. Some would even claim that's why Christ died. Whatever its origin, it's amazing the extent to which we will side-step physical discomfort. Of course, the Japanese suffer just as much as Westerners. But deep within the Japanese psyche is reverence for that bedrock of Buddhism, the inevitability of pain; the endurance of which elevates the spirit. *Gaman* enabled the Buddha Sakyamuni to sit under the bodhi tree until he achieved full enlightenment. Faint, unconscious traces of the same glorious *gaman* exists in the *Weltanschauung* of modern Japan. For instance, it would never occur to my Japanese girlfriend to shift position during a tea ceremony, even though her legs may be hurting.

I could well be drawing a long bow, but these are the thoughts I toy with whilst in hospital. I mention them only because ideas seem to have more substance when the body is immobile. As such, they form a valid part of the hospital experience.

To anyone wanting to ride a motorcycle in Japan, I'd say the most important thing to take is an attitude of wonderment. Don't let the costs discourage you. By the time I finish rehabilitating, my medical bill will be percolating over $100,000. That's a hundred grand! So before you kick-start your adventure, I'd recommend purchasing a full leather riding suit and top health insurance. There's a lot of fun to be had riding in this country. And don't worry if you can't read the street signs. For wherever you end up there will be places of interest. That even includes hospitals.

Five Stages

John McBride

First there is the entry, full of bewilderment

When I was seventeen, I won a scholarship to study Japanese language and culture for five years at a well-known university in Tokyo. Tokyo was overwhelming. I couldn't speak Japanese. The dorms were a slum. I couldn't even find a grocery store. Older students were helpful, but many were cynical and embittered about their experiences. They promised I would have to cheat to pass my exams: professors would expect me to cheat; they would even expect a gift, usually a bottle of good whiskey, before they would pass me. On and on it went. I became terribly depressed.

One of my professors did leave the room during exams so students could cheat. He knocked on the door and yelled out to let us know when he was coming back. This same professor also asked me to help him write a dictionary, which improved my Japanese language skills tremendously. For my efforts he gave me over fifty books on Japanese art history, aesthetics and philosophy — books that formed the foundation for my thesis. And I got a high mark for the course, despite my poor performance in the exams. I smile now when I look at these cherished books, and laugh at the professor banging on the door and yelling.

Eventually I moved out of the dormitory and into a sixty-year-old apartment near campus. My landlord proudly pointed to the hole in the eaves where an incendiary bomb had been dropped during the war. Tokyo was covered in snow at the time, so the attack had had a less devastating effect than it might otherwise have had. My landlord's mother had extinguished the bomb with snow and saved my apartment from the ravages of war. With the help of my landlord, I learned to replace the paper *shôji* screens, care for the wood in a traditional Japanese home and renew the *tatami* mats. I lived in this apartment happily for five years.

Next is novelty; everything is intriguing and significant

I became obsessed with geography. Behind every corner was an old Japanese building, a small *bonsai* or a place of historical interest. I pressured a geography professor into scouring Tokyo with me to find the streets of the old capital, Edo.

Edo surrounded Edo Castle, now a beautiful garden in the eastern grounds of the Imperial Palace. It extended though present-day Otemachi, and beyond, at its edges, was an old temple in which executions were performed and the spirits of the dead prevented from re-entering the city. The Bank of Japan now sits firmly in the middle of Edo's *hon-chô*. Nearby is Nihon-bashi, the bridge of Japan, and the start of the great Tokaido highway, which linked Edo with the ancient capital of Kyoto. My professor and I roamed the streets of Tokyo, now and again putting our cheeks to the bitumen to gauge the depressions in the road — telltale signs of where the ancient moat used to be.

I persuaded my professor to help me read the classical *Tokaidô-chû Hizakurige*, the comical Edo story of Yaji and Kita, two mischievous characters who travel the road from Edo to Osaka. In the spring I set out on foot to retrace their 400-kilometre journey to Kyoto. Observing an ancient curfew against travel before four o'clock in the morning, I began my journey at Nihon-bashi at four.

The Tokaido had fifty-three stations where travellers could rest, stay overnight, sample the delicacies of the region and rent chestnut-coloured mares to ease the burden of travel. The first stop on the Tokaido was Ginza, 'the silver seat', where money changers exchanged the silver-based currency of the eastern kingdom for the gold-based currency of the western.

Today the Tokaido is criss-crossed by the No.1 National highway, the Tomei and Meishin expressways, the Japan National Railway's Tokaido main line, and of course the *shinkansen* bullet train. But the old road refuses to bow to pressure from modern forces. In places, it retains the grandeur of its former self, with stately pines marking its edges and imposing mounds indicating the distance in *ri*.

In the Edo period, an acceptable fast trip was completed in sixteen days. Yaji, Kita and I did it in seventeen.

And then one is an outsider, unwanted, excluded and alone

I joined the university tennis club. I tried to be friends with everyone.

I asked my professor to teach me about Buddhist scriptures, and learned the *Hanyashingyô*, a prayer repeated by the followers of the Shingon sect of Buddhism. The

Hanyashingyô takes about five minutes to utter and embodies the principal beliefs — denial of self and all worldly chattels — of this most secretive sect. I embarked on a pilgrimage to recite the *Hanyashingyô* at the eighty-eight temples of Shikoku, established in the fourteenth century by Kobodaishi.

I shaved my head and donned pilgrim's clothes. I intended to beg for food along the way and took no money for the three-month, 1500-kilometre journey. But my professor had omitted the lesson on how to beg and by the third day I was starving. I had walked a hundred and twenty kilometres and eaten almost nothing. That night I stole 1000 yen from a temple and bought myself a meal. After filling my stomach I was overcome with guilt and returned to the temple to confess. The head priest took me in for three days, and taught me how to beg properly and how to chant the *Hanyashingyô*.

One night, as I prepared to bed down on a bench in a railway station, a young boy invited me to sleep in his house. At home, his sister graciously welcomed me and without a murmur, divided the meal she had prepared into three equal portions. Later I learned that their mother had run off. Their father was a truck driver who came home only occasionally, usually drunk. That evening he collapsed into the *futon* next to mine and snored loudly. In the morning, we ate breakfast together and the young girl packed me a lunch and sent me on my way.

The next evening, I stopped at a roadside noodle shop and asked for a bowl of noodles. The woman was only too happy to feed me, and after chatting about my pilgrimage, she offered me shelter for the night. It was *O-Bon*, and I was invited to join with her children in prayer to welcome the spirits of her dead ancestors back home. It was then I learned that the woman's husband had recently died of cancer. She faced immense difficulties, but found the kindness of heart to welcome a stranger into her home.

It is said that to do the pilgrimage, one lives the life of Kobodaishi and achieves enlightenment. I learned to spend time happily with myself, and my loneliness dissipated. I had survived on the goodwill of the people of Shikoku, and I no longer felt like an outsider.

Adjustment leads to detachment and awareness, enabling one to see beyond social and cultural structures

Being an outsider has its advantages. I pestered my professor to help me read Basho's poetry in *Oku no Hosomichi* [Far Road to the North]. The Edo poet Basho traversed the road to the northern provinces of Japan and travelled down the coast to Osaka. His poems from the trip reflect the scenery, the people and his own emotions.

I retraced his trail, read his poems, and tried to imagine what Japan might have been like in the Edo Period. And I contemplated my return to Australia too. Basho owned little, but delighted in watching people strive to be comfortable and merry. His balanced views strengthened my resolve to be unaffected by cultural barriers.

Lodging in one inn,
Together with courtesans:
Lespedeza flowers and the moon.
                              —Basho

Exhausted by journey and age, Basho died at the end of his sojourn, thus completing a life which changed the course of Japanese literature. My journey took three months, a few days shorter than Basho's.

Finally, there is departure

I decided to go to graduate school in Japan. My language skills were good and I had a large circle of friends, so there was little incentive to return home. Then I met a professor who re-opened my eyes to Australia, and to the opportunities that awaited me after my experiences in Japan.

Living in Japan for so long it is easy to get lost.

In Search of Râmen

Ralph Elliott

We turned left into Imadegawa Street where clusters of light in the distance promised food. On our right stretched the spacious grounds of Kyoto's Old Imperial Palace, mysterious in the early spring darkness.

It was our first night in Japan. Twelve hours earlier a jumbo jet from Sydney had deposited us at Narita Airport. Around us swelled a sea of smiling faces and a gabble of excited voices. We understood next to nothing, as our knowledge of Japanese was minimal: a few words of greeting, 'thank you' and 'excuse me'. Time had been too short to learn more, and I found myself wishing that I had studied Japanese, instead of Gothic, in my distant undergraduate days.

Sylvia and I had but the vaguest notions about Japanese restaurants and Japanese food. We had tasted *sushi*, but this seemed an inadequate offering to famished Australians, and so we decided to go in search of *râmen*. We knew about *râmen*, that feast of noodles with tasty-looking morsels floating in a dish of soup, because Juzo Itami's memorable film *Tampopo* had tutored us in the basics of *râmen* cooking and how to consume it without too much slurping. So we walked along Imadegawa Street looking for a place like Nobuko Miyamoto's cinematographic noodle shop, salivating in happy anticipation.

There were shops of all types: grocery shops, flower shops, chemist shops; many of them closed. But no noodle parlour.

We crossed the intersection with Kawaramachi Street and walked as far as the bridge over the Kamo River. Still no *râmen*.

But, albeit hungry, we were happy. Somehow the cool night air, the powerful sense of being enveloped by centuries of colourful history, the poignant aura of Japan — they all combined to induce a feeling of contentment, of ease of mind.

This feeling became for us, amid all the bustle of Japan's many crowded cities, the hallmark of the country and of its people. We met it whenever we stepped from a busy thoroughfare in Tokyo or Nagoya into a homely side street. It greeted us in the sudden, embracing tranquillity of every shrine or temple garden. We found it among the peacefully nibbling deer at Nara and amid the breathtaking beauty of Miyajima. We felt it, most poignantly, among the fountains and extensive flower beds surrounding the Hiroshima Peace Museum.

There rests, in the grounds of Kyoto's Ryoanji Temple, a *tsukubai* stone basin, inscribed with four characters that spell the Zen message 'I learn only to be contented'. The message had a familiar ring, for it echoed what St Paul had written in one of his letters: 'I have learned, in whatsoever state I am, therewith to be content', an unexpected spiritual meeting of East and West.

Some time later, when I first came across the treasury of ancient verses in the *Man'yôshû*, I found one little poem by Otomo no Tabito — an almost exact contemporary of the Venerable Bede — which expresses in more picturesque but no less succinct mode this same sense of present contentment:

If, here and now, I'm happy,
It were indeed absurd
To worry lest, in some next life,
I prove an ant or bird.

Well, we did not turn into ants or birds in the weeks that followed our landing in Japan. Nor did we worry that we might return hungry to our hostelry on this or any other night.

We thought it advisable, however, to retrace our steps before venturing too far into as yet unknown quarters of Kyoto. Before long we came to another busy intersection and turned into Karasuma Street, as here were yet more lights promising nourishment.

And then, suddenly, crowded together, a congregation of intimate restaurants, their windows offering untold gastronomic delights made of richly coloured plastic. We could read the prices, of course, and in a few places the Japanese names had been thoughtfully translated into English. We gazed at them in wonder, uncomprehendingly, because the words remained mysterious. We could at least compare prices: there was a bowl of *oyako-don* at 700 yen, an assortment of dishes called *tonkatsu teishoku* at 1,100 yen, and an even more tempting-looking miscellany, *mizutaki*, at what seemed a princely 2,500 yen.

We kept searching for *râmen*, our gastronomic life-belt, but when at last we spotted its plastic image it had, alas, none of the mystique of *Tampopo*. Indeed, it looked so disappointing, so prosaic, so particularly plastic, that we turned sadly away. Itami's masterpiece had not prepared us for this inedible polychromatic sculpture, nor had it instructed us to distinguish the respective ingredients of the exotic dishes we were surveying, let alone enable us to foresee how well our untutored maws might accommodate such unfamiliar fare.

We turned back along Karasuma Street, on the other side, too timid, be it confessed, on this first night to bravely face the culinary unknown.

And then we saw it.

Incredulous we gazed at the large illuminated **M** beckoning round a corner, the familiar logo advertising a McDonald's Family Restaurant. McDonald's in the heart of old Imperial Japan? Was it a mirage? A dream? A false creation proceeding, like Macbeth's dagger, from the hunger-oppresséd brain? No. It was real; it was palpable; and it was Japanese.

We went in.

The furnishings were as familiar as in the drive-in McDonald's at our local shopping centre. The pretty girls behind the counter wore the familiar uniforms, and above their heads were all the well-known pictures: the Big Macs and all the lesser Macs, the chicken pieces, the potato chips, even the apple pies in their cardboard wrappers.

The search for *râmen* was forgotten as we pointed at the giant likenesses painted on the wall. The young ladies smiled and bowed demurely as we handed over hundreds of yen and carried our Macs to a table. Once again East and West were harmoniously united. We slept contentedly that first night in Kyoto, although our lack of alimentary courage, our craven capitulation to Mac instead of *râmen* troubled my dreams and I awoke to vow to Sylvia and myself that henceforth we would plunge, mouth first, into every *sushi* or *teppan-yaki,* or even *sukiyaki* (when feeling more than usually extravagant), that beckoned through a window.

For we soon discovered the joys, the tasty, savoury, piquant, palatable joys of Japanese cuisine, of which *Tampopo* had offered a mere hors d'oeuvre, a celluloid prelude.

Can there be anything more delightful, more conducive to perfect contentment, than to be greeted by a smiling, bowing young woman with a complimentary cup of green tea as you anticipate the delicacies offered in a variety of dainty dishes of a *teishoku*? And not only in the intimacy of a tastefully decorated restaurant, but no less in the comfort of the *shinkansen* as it bears you smoothly at great speed through the changing landscapes of Honshu or Kyushu.

As we journeyed up and down the country, we grew to love Japan, its cities and its paddy fields, its ornate temples and ancient castles, and not least its picturesque gardens, from the intimate miniature of a domestic setting to the breathtaking grandeur of Tokyo's Kiyosumi Garden, not forgetting Thomas Glover's unexpected garden overlooking Nagasaki Harbour, another convergence of East and West.

And wherever we went the kindness and hospitality of Japanese colleagues and their families overwhelmed us. We ate with them and we drank with them. Many a time and oft did we enjoy our sips of *sake* or a few glasses of Sapporo Lion beer with newfound friends, in the comfort of Tokyo's International House, in the luxurious setting of some grand hotel, or, best of all, in the intimacy of a family home. We learnt how to dispose our legs at low tables, and how to say '*Itadakimasu*' before a meal and '*Gochisô-sama*' after it.

But above all we drank in, we imbibed, we consumed with passion the spirit of Japan, making friends, contemplating with reverence the magnificent Buddha at Nara, watching the steam clouds rise above Mount Aso, or languidly surveying the pleasant scenery while on a Yanagawa River cruise. We milled with the crowds in the busy Ginza and found ourselves mobbed for autographs by scores of schoolchildren at Nijo Castle. We were spellbound (and slightly puzzled) by the histrionics of Mokuami Kawatake's *The Five Thieves* at the Kabukiza Theatre, and we were enchanted by young Michiko's singing Schubert, Brahms and Mozart in the homely seclusion of our host's apartment.

Our search for *râmen* had led us not so much to a noodle parlour in nocturnal Kyoto as to the hearts of a courteous, generous, hard-working people who have managed to retain, amid all the business, the feverish fret, of a modern society with all its Western appurtenances, much of the grace and graciousness of Murasaki's courtly *Tale of Genji*, of Utamaro's exotic beauties and Hokusai's startling landscapes.

The memories we took back home with us are too numerous to mention. We did taste our dish of *râmen* and enjoyed it. That McDonald's should be part of these memories is perhaps as symbolic of modern Japan as is the Daihatsu car Sylvia now drives with pleasure along Australian roads.

At the back of our Australian house there is now a small Japanese garden, whose annual cherry blossoms are happy reminders of the avenue of trees we admired on an April morning along the banks of the Kamo River. And close to a low lantern, facing blooming azaleas, by a bed of lovingly raked gravel, a block of stone bears an inscription in four characters. It reads: 'I learn only to be contented'. On the groundwork of St Paul's Epistle an edifice of contentment has been built in our lives which we owe not so much to our search for *râmen* as to our quest for the soul of Japan.

Foreign Wives

Cory Taylor

O n a close, grey day, when the Japanese countryside labours to breathe under its burden of highways, power lines, traffic and buildings, Elena put a tray of chicken fillets into the oven for lunch.

'People ask me why I married someone I'd only known for three weeks', she said, laughing. 'I don't know why. You do get to know someone very well through letters. And we were young and stupid', she added, without bitterness. 'And so here I am.'

She made the story very short. She had, after all, only one point to make: She had survived Japan.

'When I first came here from Bucharest it was terrible. I wouldn't go out because the children shouted at me: "Foreigner! Foreigner!" My husband worked very long hours at a company, and so I was home all day by myself, afraid to go outside. I hated Japan. I didn't want to learn Japanese because I hated Japan so much. I didn't want children. I didn't want them to suffer all that. We were living in a flat with a timber yard on one side and another timber yard on the other side and it was only quiet after eight o'clock in the evening, but I had the saws going in my head all night. It was hell. About five years ago, I went to a party on New Year's Eve and I stayed out all night. It was so much fun to be with foreigners. An American man said to me: "You've been in Japan all these years and you're still sane!" "Yes", I said. And I felt quite proud. He was showing me respect. Just for being here!'

I respected her too. I wanted to run away already and I'd only been in Japan for two weeks. I was in a desperate mood as we drove to Elena's house. My husband had been silent the whole way and the children had sat in the back of the car complaining and holding their noses. I knew what my husband was thinking: Are we going to last? Can we look at this every day and not die from the sheer ugliness of it? Inland Australian Aborigines transported to the coast reportedly dropped dead at the sight of the sea. So it could be with us. The sight of the chaotic tangle of grey, man-made rubble and the stench of the piggeries alongside the highway might prove fatal. We had left, only days before, our house in Surfer's Paradise: lushly surrounded by poincianas and paw paw and umbrella trees, festooned on warm evenings with iridescent green lorikeets; a river at the front of the garden, beyond the swimming pool, where the boys caught greedy puffer fish in butterfly nets. There was no doubt we were all pining.

But I was not just homesick: I was lost, literally lost. I barely knew my address and I couldn't recite my phone number. Had anyone asked me to look at a map of the city, I could not have directed them to my home. I had arrived in Japan and been abruptly thrown into a childlike state of illiteracy, regularly reminded of my helpless inadequacy in a complex and unfamiliar world. Like a child, I was anxious not to be abandoned. That's why my husband came with me to Elena's. Without him I would have panicked. I would have come straight home while I could still see where it was; the child who only ventures as far as the forest edge before taking fright and fleeing back to her own garden.

After two wrong turns my husband stopped at a small wooden house which clung to the roadside like a shipwreck. The foreigner apparently lived in the white house on the edge of the wheat field we had just passed. By the time we turned, Elena was outside waiting for us — obviously the foreigner; tall, fair-haired and unlike anyone I'd seen since we had arrived. A foreign woman was a rarity in the countryside, yet there she was, standing weirdly across the field of young wheat, as visibly excited to see me as I was to see her.

Elena was the local representative of the Association of Foreign Wives Married to Japanese, and the only one in the whole prefecture, it seemed. She didn't just grill chicken for lunch. She made small fried meatballs, a bean sprout salad, egg rolls for the children, balls of rice wrapped in seaweed, a loaf of freshly baked bread, a chocolate cake with strawberries and kiwi fruit. She was well-organised; she worked methodically without attenuated debris and she knew what would happen next. Elena had learned to cook, she explained, by watching cookery courses on television. That accounted for her poise. Her attention seemed to be on what she was saying so unguardedly, rather than on what she was doing with so little apparent effort.

'I was so depressed a few years ago, when my children were still very small, that I went to a psychiatrist and asked what was wrong with me. At first she gave me some medicine and that was terrible. It made me sleepy and sick all day, and I had to work and look after my children. My husband wasn't working then. He dreams. Well, we're both dreamers, but I have to put food on the table. So I told her the medicine was no good. It made me worse than I was before, so she stopped it. And then I kept going to her for two years and I told her many things about my feelings and my life and in the end she told me there was nothing wrong with me. She said: "There is nothing wrong with you. You are just different. You just have to accept it". But it didn't help me very much to be told that. It is very hard being different in Japan. Impossible. And so then I asked myself all the time: Why am I here like an exile? I didn't do anything criminal to be sent here!' She laughed. Her teeth were neglected and the gums were swelling a little.

'I am forty-five now. I'm getting old. My mother says I must think about where I want to die. Helena, who is coming to lunch too, is from Slovenia. She went back for two months last year and bought an apartment and furniture and clothes — everything. She wants to die there, not here. I don't know. I haven't really thought about it. Japanese friends say to me: "You're so Japanese!" You know the way they do, as if you're some kind of miracle. But of course I'm not Japanese. I had my life in Bucharest. Not such a bad life. And everything is so different there now. I think I should go back and find out who I was before I married. I think it's time I did that. And I want to go to England before I die. I studied about English culture and literature all those years ago. I want to see it for myself. Maybe I'll go this year before it's too late.'

Helena had let herself in. She appeared in the kitchen in a jogging suit, flushed and sturdy, with fierce, dark blue eyes. 'Of course you will go this year', she said. 'You must! It will make you feel much better.'

She was like a sports mistress suggesting a run around the oval.

Now there were three of us — foreign wives — a kind of secret clan gathering.

'Helena has survived here for as long as I have', Elena said, introducing us. 'And she isn't crazy either.'

'Don't believe a word she says', Helena said, laughing with her whole big rosy face. 'We're both mad. We must be. We're still here.'

She apologised for her jogging suit but she hadn't had time to change. Helena was married to a high school teacher and she, like Elena, was an English teacher. Helena had a teenage son and a daughter of ten. Elena had a boy of nine and a girl of just four who was already embarked on her six-day-a-week kindergarten career. Elena showed me a photograph of her children and told me, almost apologetically, how very Japanese they both looked, as if it were a failing on her part.

'Of course they are completely Japanese children', she said, 'in the way they think'. She brought her hands up to her face and enclosed it, blocking her view to either side.

Helena grimaced. 'Mine too', she said. 'I couldn't even get them to come to Slovenia with me. They didn't want to miss school. "No one misses school Mum", they said, and that was that. No more discussion.'

'My husband says the same', said Elena. 'He's very Japanese. Well, he's not Japanese, but he is. Do you know what I mean?'

I did know what she meant. The state of being Japanese was often discussed in this way, as if it were some persistent condition, the symptoms of which flared up under certain provocations. In men the symptoms could be fairly unpleasant, involving attacks of black obstinate orthodoxy, even in the most well-travelled and enlightened. In women the condition tended to be well-regarded — like pregnancy. To be told one was Japanese implied that one was pleasantly subdued and compliant, sensitive to the needs of others and selfless in their diligent fulfilment.

After lunch Elena's husband and mine took the children out for a walk along the river. It was still oppressively grey outside and on every horizon a webbing of power lines ensnared the landscape in a huge net, like an aviary for some ferocious bird species. Inside the aviary it was possible to catch intimations of wild solitude, but not for long. After the children got out of school, the river paths bustled with flocks of students on bicycles, their black plumage handsome and sombre against the tawny grasses of the riverbank.

'The hardest thing to get used to is the look of it', I said. 'It's all so ugly.'

They both laughed, as if I'd made some hilarious admission, which left them free to reciprocate.

'Isn't it!' they chorused.

Elena's expression became impassioned. 'And they were free all this time. They didn't have to build everything everywhere. They weren't communists. They didn't have the excuse. Why did they make such a mess?'

There was no answer except that Japan's priorities had been otherwise arranged. Indiscriminate development had decimated most of the country's flat land.

Elena sighed and started to clear the dishes. We made gestures towards departing. 'Coffee?', Elena asked.

Helena rubbed her hands together greedily. 'The coffee here's very good. She has a secret.'

'I can't live without coffee', said Elena. 'It keeps me breathing.' She ground the beans in a coffee grinder she had brought with her from Romania, a heavy cylindrical instrument polished clean and steely by constant use. 'It's over a hundred years old', said Elena, turning it with force and releasing its enticing breath into the air. The grinder had made its dumb migration through time and space with enviable calm. Incapable of anguish, it was patently far more likely than any of us to endure.

The coffee spilled over into the saucer as she poured it. Elena told me it meant I'd be happy. Romanians apparently had the knack of reading the future in coffee grounds.

'It's what she tells everyone', Helena said. 'She's an optimist.'

The men were back sooner than expected. They hung around the door, hesitating to take the children's shoes off when they judged we were so close to leaving, or should be.

Elena lowered her voice and leaned towards me across the table. 'There's one thing I want to say to you before you go', she said. 'Be careful of your children. They are so open and natural and full of life. Just watch that they don't become narrow and afraid to be different. Because it happens. It's happened to mine and it's terrible. I want to get them out of here and show them that there is another world and other ways to be and other ways to think. I want to open them up before it's too late. To open their eyes.'

Helena gazed out the window and nodded her head.

'Shall we go?' my husband called hopefully.

We found our way back to the highway, naming the landmarks I would need to remember if I was to come to Elena's again by myself: the wholesale vegetable market at the light, the cream-coloured snack bar on the next corner, the sports clothing store, the used car yard, the *pachinko* parlour, the noodle shop. It was a lot to remember. I had the feeling I might never find Elena again, that she and Helena might be swallowed up in our wake and become irretrievably of the past; had I blundered into a dense thicket constructed along quasi-organic principles I wasn't equipped to understand? I felt in my pocket for the piece of paper on which I'd written their phone numbers.

'Why is it so smoky everywhere?' my son asked from the back of the car. 'Why can't I see anything?'

We were passing small plots of fog-bound apple trees, all blanketed in blue netting to keep the birds out, each apple ripening in its own individual wrapping. The trees quickly gave way to car yards.

'The wind from the mountains will come and blow the smoke away', I said.

'When?' he asked.

'Soon', I said.

'I can't see any mountains', he said.

'Keep looking', I said.

Tokyo Cats

Ben Middleton

I slipped out my door into the drabness of another Tokyo winter evening, and down the narrow alley that led along the side of my apartment block. The alley, hardly used any more, housed piles of junk — a stripped-down Honda 250, an old refrigerator, a few stray tom-cats. I liked the atmosphere of my neighbourhood. The spirit of another era somehow lingered on, giving it the feel of a scene from an old sepia ink photograph.

I jumped on a train headed for Shinjuku and flicked through an *Akira* comic book that someone had left behind. There's nothing like a bit of sex-n-violence-n-anti-establishment humour while you're on the train. Nothing like Tokyo style cynicism either. At Shinjuku, I side-stepped my way through the late night crowd, fighting every inch of the way through a gaggle of *bodi-con* girls, to the Chuo line platform; waiting, waiting for the yellow train to come and take me to see my girl.

The audience was just starting to pour out of the Akashi Theatre when I arrived. They were mostly students, abuzz after the show. The distorted groove of 'Flippers Guitar' resonated from boom boxes in the cramped foyer. The manager, a real cool dude in his early forties, with long hair and flares, grinned and thanked me for the bottle of whiskey I brought him last time. We promised to go drinking again soon. I headed backstage and down the corridor to Mina's room. She was just wiping off the grease-paint when I arrived.

'How'd it go babe?'

'Bitchin'.'

The chill air bit our skin when we emerged, but it felt good. I stopped to buy a packet of Indonesian kretek cigarettes from a vending machine, one of the few places in Tokyo you can get them. You can get anything you want in Tokyo if you have the money and the know-how. Anything. Mina and I shot around a few corners and into our favourite jazz bar, the Jirokichi.

We could hear the sax wailing as we paid at the door. That cat that was blowin' had it, and looking around the tiny room, everyone knew it. Wah-wah-wah went the sax, as bodies ground to the beat on the dance floor. A big bear of a man belted a pock-marked drum kit as though nothing else mattered. Hell, at that moment, nothing else did matter. Yah-yeah, yah-yeah went the drums, then they both cut, and the bass started to sing, real lyrical. On the dance floor, everybody swayed. Then the tenor sax came back in, driving low. Baugh, baugh, baugh, baugh. Circling higher in crescendo. Eeeee! You could feel it in your bones.

The room wasn't big enough for all the people out for a good time, and the atmosphere hit us hard as we went downstairs to the bar. This band believed in the old wall of sound theory. They were playing it sweet too. We ordered a couple of Wild Turkeys and sat for a while just digging the groove. A cloud of tobacco fumes hung over the room.

Mina gave me one of her looks, and we moved to the dance space. The music was sweet, so sweet, but it couldn't mask the heady layer of violence and energy that lay beneath its surface. That's what gave it its power. It's the source of the addiction; the feel of Tokyo. We danced like we wanted to live the impossible.

Then it was over. Soaking wet, we let out our breath. It felt good to have danced. It was just on midnight, and the young crowd started to trickle out. Half of Tokyo must have been intoxicated and rushing like rats to the station to cram into the last train. We went out too, but not to the station. We headed around to an underground club called the Pumpkin Bar, a mellow place to hang for those who dug jazz.

You see, there are two genres of jazz bars in Tokyo. The first, like the good ol' Blind Cat, just behind Shinjuku Station, are hot. They're full of people and play just about anything. Anything jazz, that is. The old Cat is tiny. There ain't hardly room inside to swing a dead cat around by the tail, but it's packed full every night, with trendy business types mostly, and students and the occasional 'office lady'.

Then there's the second type, like the Pumpkin Bar. It's cool. Not cool in the everyday sense, but cool in the narrow, technical sense. The decor is minimalist; very urban, very black, very hip. You don't tap your foot to the beat of the music in the Pumpkin. No sir, you sit and just feel the vibes, internalise them. You feel them deep, but you don't hardly show no emotion. It's the kind of place for serious conversation in quiet tones. If you want to yell and get excited about politics or love or poetry or whatever, you go to the old Cat. But if you just want to chill, then you go to a joint like the Pumpkin. That's why we were there. We just wanted to sit and talk after our rave.

Mina felt like *mâbo-dôfu*, which was too proletarian to be on the menu at the Pumpkin. Apart from a few other bars, not too much was open in Koenji at four in the morning. So we made our way over to a rougher part of town to just the place. The spartan interior — a white tiled floor, cheap plastic chairs, a few scattered laminated tables, all bathed in fluorescent light — didn't seem too appealing, but Mina assured me that the food was good, and it was. Lotsa chilli.

But the place wasn't happening, so we decided to go and see our friend, the master of the Elephant, or Zo-san, another bar. It hid itself away in a back street, near most of the live houses. We were greeted by the sounds of Robert Fripp and King Crimson. Some school kids were going for it in one of the rear booths, but nobody paid any attention. The master was a real psychedelic child who dug the beat of the sixties. He also moonlighted as a drummer in a heavy metal band, something of an absolutely-contradictory-self-identity, you might say. He had spirals of long, long hair, which reached half-way down his back, mostly dyed red. It went down a real treat with his tight green Levis. He was good for a joke and I liked the way his laugh kinda hissed out the side of his mouth. We pushed aside a few well-thumbed copies of the cult mag *Takarajima* and sat down at the bar to be entertained until about half five, when we were too tired and too drunk to cope with any more.

We headed out into the dawn and hopped what must have been the first train of the day, empty, except for a few eager-beaver salarymen, asleep in their early edition news-papers. Mina pulled the collar of her coat up around her ears and fell asleep against my shoulder. The train roared back towards Shinjuku. Back towards home.

Ganbatte!

Susan McAlister Akikusa

It is still early in the afternoon, but I am bone-weary, barely aware that I am travelling at great speed, and some thousands of metres up in the air, from Tokyo to the far northern city of Sapporo.

From time to time, my fellow passengers are giving me odd looks. I suspect this is because my overnight bag, stowed dutifully under the seat in front of me, is emitting a steady stream of loud chirps. The noise is all that's keeping me awake.

My thoughts keep wandering back to earlier in the day, to just after midnight, when I had been sitting in the back of a black, chauffeur-driven limousine, cruising the streets of Ginza. With me was my husband and a friend of his, Yamauchi-san, the vice president of one of Japan's biggest media networks. It was his limo and his chauffeur, and he therefore had us at his mercy.

At this point, my reminiscences are interrupted by a flight attendant, who arrives at my side just as I am furtively stuffing some of the airline salad into my overnight bag.

She smiles politely, but appears disconcerted as the chirruping from the bag reaches a crescendo, then subsides into a series of clicks and cheeps. Not for the first time, my Japanese husband looks away and pretends not to know the foreign woman seated beside him.

The evening with Yamauchi-san was a frenetic progression from one night-spot to another. Midnight approached, but his pace did not slacken: there were more whiskeys and rice wines, more introductions to other businessmen and politicians, more clubs and bars, still more whiskeys and rice wines, and on, and on, and on, until it all became a noisy, boozy blur.

At about 2 a.m., sensing that our enthusiasm was waning, a still exuberant Yamauchi-san declared the evening at an end. However, he directed us away from the waiting limo and towards a collection of street vendors, most of whom were perched on little stools, managing, as only the Japanese can, to sit upright while fast asleep. To mark the occasion, Yamauchi-san bought from one of the vendors a clear plastic container, about half the size of a shoe box, with a handle and tiny air vents on the lid. This he presented to me, with something of a flourish. Inside, on the bottom, were pieces of green vegetables, and, hopping around and chirruping for all they were worth, six crickets.

As I received the gift and mumbled some words of appreciation, I swayed slightly and leaned against the street-cart for support. Yamauchi-san smiled and shook his head at this display of weakness. '*Ganbatte kudasai*', he said: Come on, keep going! '*Ganbatte!*'

Within hours, Yamauchi-san would be at his desk, directing one of the world's major media conglomerates. He spent every night as he had spent this one, and every morning he showed up for work at 7 a.m., on the dot.

My husband told me that, once, a technician working for Yamauchi-san's network at a remote relay station had failed to throw a switch at the right time, and about two minutes of a radio program were lost to the handful of inhabitants of an island closer to Siberia than Tokyo. A hastily convened managerial board meeting refused Yamauchi-san's offer to resign over the incident, but it did require some form of atonement. It made him take two days off work.

This was hard, very hard. He spent forty-eight idle hours in his small apartment with his wife and children, and he suffered through every minute. It probably wasn't much fun for them, either.

Now, as I slump in my aircraft seat, the crickets twittering at my feet and the big, northern island of Hokkaido spreading beyond the window, the frenetic days and even more frenetic nights of Tokyo seem far away. Yamauchi-san told me that Hokkaido is Japan's Alaska: big, majestically mountainous, heavily forested and underpopulated. The people there, he said, are considered by other Japanese to be a bit slow and provincial.

Yamauchi-san added that he had never been to Hokkaido. He does not consider this a loss.

After our plane lands, I wake up sufficiently to climb on a bus and head off for the resort of Toya-ko. Inside my overnight bag, the crickets are still chirruping, and my fellow passengers are giving me looks which are, by now, becoming familiar. As I peer into the plastic box, I notice that one cricket is missing. I count them, and count again. Only five present: one must have escaped. Then I see the remains of a leg in a corner, and realise that the missing cricket has been eaten by its fellows during the flight from Tokyo.

'They must have been very stressed', I say, as I show my husband the box and its contents. 'They probably didn't like the airline food', he replies.

From Sapporo, we drive for several hours through deep valleys and past volcanoes whose cones rise elegantly into the clear sky, like replicas of Mount Fuji. Some are capped with glistening snow, even though this is midsummer. A fox darts through the grass beside the road and swans fly overhead.

Toya-ko is a deep blue lake dotted with wooded islets roamed by deer. As we arrive, the lake is a picture of azure tranquillity, surrounded by high green hills and masses of the most brilliantly coloured hydrangeas I have ever seen. Towering above the resort town is a mountain, Usu, whose steep flanks are covered with pines and bamboo thickets.

We get out of the bus and begin to climb the steep road leading up the mountain side towards our hotel, the Toya-ko National Health Resort, which is famed for its hot springs. Here we are to spend several days recovering from the excesses of Tokyo. As we walk, I look up and notice that Mount Usu's summit is not green. It is black, and instead of trees, it appears to be dotted with matchsticks.

When I point this out to my husband, he says, nonchalantly, that Usu is an active volcano, which last erupted three years ago, covering the town with ash. Fortunately, the lava and a torrent of boiling mud flowed down the other side of the mountain. Encouraged to continue when I make no response, he turns and points to the wide, circular lake below. 'The water', he says, 'is actually lying inside a caldera above a really huge volcano: Usu is just one of its vents'. 'Well, fancy that', I reply, uncharacteristically at a loss for words.

That night, as we prepare to go to sleep on the *futons* a maid has spread for us over the *tatami* mats in our room, I try to mute the racket from the still chirruping crickets by putting their container into a cupboard under a pile of unused linen. Next morning, although the noise level seems unabated, the number of crickets is down to four, and I am not in the least sorry to leave these aggressive little creatures behind when we set out for a nearby tourist attraction. As we ride in the bus, my husband tells me a story.

The soil around Toya-ko is volcanic and rich, and a handful of neat farms, which grow potatoes and the succulent asparagus for which Hokkaido is renowned, quilt the few stretches of relatively flat, open countryside that exist amid the steep hills and the thick, dark forests of pine, oak and maple.

Early one morning, an elderly farmer walked out in a low-lying mist to inspect his potato crop and noticed a small bump in his field. It looked like the crown of a helmet emerging from the soil. This gave the farmer quite a start, because his nation was fighting a great war against a powerful enemy who, he had heard, was bent on destroying Japan and the Japanese people. The Showa god-emperor, whom the enemy disrespectfully called by his name, Hirohito, had need of every man capable of bearing arms to assist in the defence of his realm, and for one ghastly moment the farmer thought a long-dead *samurai* was rising from the earth to join the fray.

However, when the farmer gingerly pushed the bump with the toe of his straw sandal, it turned out to be made of nothing but dirt. He forgot about it.

Some days later, however, the bump appeared to be bigger. The farmer examined it, and, yes, it was definitely higher than before. Somewhere underneath, he decided, there must be an exceptionally large potato.

Over the next few weeks, the bump continued to grow, until it was about half a metre high. At this point, the farmer had to admit that it probably didn't contain a potato, even if it was, as he'd begun to hope, the world's largest potato. Perhaps it was an ant hill. He watched it for several days, but no ants appeared, and he changed his mind again. It must have been the work of a mole. A very big mole, too, because by now, the bump had turned into a mound close to a metre high.

When the mound reached, then passed, a metre in height, it occurred to the farmer that it might not be the work of a mole. A bigger animal was called for. A badger, perhaps? A bear? And so, the weeks and then the months went by, and as the war approached its climax, while armies collapsed, fleets sank, and great cities to the south were blasted and razed from the face of the earth, the farmer quietly watched his mound grow ever higher. In fact, the entire potato field was now being lifted, and the farmer's little wood and paper house was developing an alarming tilt. He asked for advice from his neighbours and they confirmed what he had already begun to suspect: he wasn't growing potatoes any more, he was growing a mountain.

This was distressing news. A potato farmer is meant to grow potatoes, but now he couldn't, and this depressed and frustrated him. He fretted in particular about not being able to help feed his countrymen, millions of whom were starving. Yet, the farmer didn't rail against his misfortune, or seek help from the authorities or anyone else. 'Ganbatte', he said to himself. Keep your chin up: 'Ganbatte ne!'.

One day, he received an offer to buy his land from the local postmaster, who was about to retire and was at a loss for something to do with the rest of his life. The farmer accepted, and promptly removed himself to another part of Hokkaido, where he settled down to grow something less intimidating.

The bespectacled postmaster, who had never grown anything, was pleased to see the mountain continue to rise. By now, it had a name, Showa-Shinzan, in honour of the Emperor. No one knows what the Emperor thought of this, for he was at that time somewhat preoccupied with other matters.

The postmaster acquired books and diagrams, built equipment, kept records, studied night and day, and watched, and watched, and watched. No father ever paid his firstborn child more attention. He retired as postmaster, and began a new career as a vulcanologist.

His knowledge grew with the mountain: his writing on the subject was original and erudite, and became widely admired. His name, Mimatsu-san, began to appear in learned journals outside his homeland.

In 1948, a conference attended by the world's leading vulcanologists was held in Oslo, and the former postmaster was invited to present a paper. The delegates were so impressed with his meticulous observations that they conferred scientific immortality upon him by formally naming and adopting the Mimatsu Diagram, this being the former postmaster's unique cross-sectional depiction of the evolution of a volcano.

'And, there it is', says my husband, pointing towards what used to be a potato field and is now a towering mass of hardened magma, over four hundred metres in height, its peak only intermittently visible amid roiling clouds of gas and steam.

We leave the bus and walk a short distance to the foot of Showa-Shinzan. The mountain's bare, dark brown sides are streaked and blotched with red and orange, and spiked with pinnacles of blackened rock; streams of yellow and pale green liquid bubble from fissures and pits and ooze past strange, jagged lava forms, down cliffs and around heaps of boulders to form stinking pools at its base. The mountain is warm to the touch and breathes out streams of vapour as though it were a living thing. It may not be the world's largest potato, but it is undeniably impressive.

That evening, as we open the door to our hotel room, we are met by a barrage of chirps and clicks. I peer into the container, and note that nearly all the vegetables are gone. So is another cricket.

'Why are they doing this?' I cry in desperation. 'They can't help themselves', my husband mutters, 'they're from Tokyo'.

That night, after dinner, we are lying on our *futons*, reading, when I notice something odd. Although the crickets have once again been consigned to the cupboard, we should still be able to hear their muffled chirruping. But, now, there is silence. I slide the cupboard door open and remove the container, and the three surviving insects are all there, upright, antennas waving, but silent. I put them beside my *futon*, and resume reading.

About half an hour later, the floor shudders for several seconds. I have experienced earth tremors in Japan before, so I am not alarmed. Some ten minutes later, there is another, stronger, shudder. Then another, and another, each burst of movement longer and fiercer than the one before. Finally, the floor rocks so violently that I roll off my *futon*. Somewhere, a woman screams. My husband says not to worry, that this is probably as bad as it will get, but just the same, he dashes for the door and slides it open, so it cannot jam and trap us in our room if things get worse.

They do. At first, I think a plane is flying into our hotel, so loud is the roar which engulfs us. The floor is jolted up, then sideways, and I am flung about like a child in a dodgem car. The roar increases, and the room judders ever more violently. A crack appears in the wall near the floor and shoots up to the ceiling. The hotel must surely collapse. Then, as though a switch has been turned off, the roaring and shaking stop. For several more hours there are after-shocks, some of them quite severe, but they gradually peter out, and it seems, finally, that the earthquake is over.

The Toya-ko National Health Resort, like most Japanese buildings, is as quake-proof as possible. Even so, it now has many more cracks than it had a day before. There's also a lot of broken crockery, chairs and tables are not where they were a few hours ago, and wall hangings are lying on the floor. However, the staff assure us that all is well. It happens fairly regularly, they say, though this was a bit rougher than usual. It's not really an earthquake, they explain, it's the volcano, Usu. It wakes up, gets restless and lets off a bit of steam now and then. That's all.

After a sleepless night, I pack up and trudge into town with my husband to catch a bus for Sapporo. The townsfolk had begun to clear up at first light, and almost all evidence of last night's violence is gone. Everything is back to normal. '*Ganbatte*.' Keep going. Don't give in. Make the most of things. '*Ganbatte kudasai*.' Life goes on as usual.

Except for the crickets. There are, to my surprise, still three of them sitting in their container; no one has been eaten during the night. And they are still silent, and remain so all the way back to Tokyo. In fact, to my great relief, they never chirp again.

Nightlife

Angela Snedden

S o much has been said about the evils of working as a
hostess in Japan. But it was the night people who made
my experience of that country so special.

I had always thought Japan was the land of 'no sex, no
drugs, no wine, no women . . .', just like that song said. I
was twenty-one; a blonde-haired, blue-eyed female, world-
weary and desperately in need of a change. So I arranged
a working holiday visa to Japan, land of mystery and
intrigue, and made plans to study *ikebana*, Japanese cooking and perhaps *karate*. I wanted a year of cultural immer-
sion and intensive language study: I would live a pure and
simple Buddhist life and be a model foreigner.

And so life began. My host family in Shizuoka were
lovely, but they kept me on a tight rein. A year in Japan felt
like something to be endured. The language barrier was
overwhelming and I had very few opportunities to meet
other young people. Soon, however, it became obvious to
my family that I was very lonely. So my host father
arranged for me to join a cultural exchange program run by

the Junior Chamber of Commerce. At first it seemed just like a Rotary Club for young people, but that perception changed very quickly.

I was invited to their annual party and being extra careful not to offend, I keenly accepted. On the day of the party, fearing total boredom, I invited another Australian girl, Penny, to come along.

As we approached the party, music and revelry oozed from the building. We stepped off the lift to find the rooftop awash with activity — there must have been 400 men in fancy dress, some in drag, some wearing barely anything at all. People were consuming copious amounts of beer, dancing on tables, singing, shouting and having a wild time. Surely this couldn't be Japan! After a beer or two it hit me that this *was* Japan, and I suddenly realised that I had never been to such a good party in Australia.

Penny and I had a wonderful time. A Japanese band played Beatles covers and Filipina show-girls entertained the crowd until the party wound down early in the morning. Not wanting to let such a fun night end, we said our polite goodbyes and hit the neon-lit streets in search of a place to dance.

We wandered though tiny alleyways until we heard loud music coming from the upper floors of a narrow building. Fear of the omnipresent arbitrary pricing scale should have been enough to invoke common sense at this point, but we were undeterred. Into the building and up the stairs we marched in true naive foreigner style.

We were greeted at the door by a pretty yet somewhat unusual creature in *kimono*. She escorted us down a corridor and into a room abuzz with music and merriment. Before we knew what was happening, we had been seated and two glasses of the infamous *mizu wari* (scotch and water) were put before us on the bar. In front of us stood a transvestite (*okama*), doing a striptease to Madonna's 'Like a Virgin'. When he got down to the bare essentials, his private parts began to sparkle and three small fire crackers ignited. When he shook them all about, Penny and I suddenly realised all the hostesses were men!

From that night on the nightlife of Japan became my passion. I became a hostess and befriended some of the most interesting characters. One of my favourites was Po-chan, a 70-year-old *okama*.

Po-chan made up his face and bald head like KISS, and wore lamé evening gowns with high heels and stockings. His look was stunning, but Po-chan's accessories were the true signature of his art. Po-chan took great delight in parodying Japanese women's obsession with brand names. On his most famous handbag he had written '*cha-neru*' in bold black *kanji*. When read in Japanese it sounds like 'Chanel'.

What impressed me most about the night world of Japan is the genuine acceptance of eccentric characters like Po-chan by Japanese people. In Australia, people who dare to be different are ridiculed, yet in Japan businessmen pay good money to be entertained. Herein lies the essence of what sets Japan apart: it is the childlike innocence of Japanese people which makes going to a love hotel natural and not sleazy, working in a hostess bar fun and not a chore, and socialising an absolute pleasure. Japan's underworld is not sleazy; it is merely a harmless playground for adults.

Putting a Foot Wrong in Rural Japan

Alan Elliott

One of the many pleasures of Japan is its *minshuku* accommodation. The traditional *ryokan* may be charming, the service attentive, the food exquisite, the experience memorable — and the bill often astronomical. But the meals are brought to the room, so you may stay for a week and the only person you see is the maid. In contrast, a good *minshuku* is a warm, friendly and relatively inexpensive place where meals are eaten in the communal dining room with the family and the other guests, and one may savour the experience of living the way Japanese people live. In return it is polite to lay out and put away the *futon*, to serve oneself at meals and so on. After dinner, over a *tokkuri* or two of *sake* or a few glasses of beer, there may be an interesting discussion or perhaps the host or hostess will be persuaded to sing some local songs. Give me a good *minshuku* every time! One of many which come to mind is to be found in a town on the Japan Sea coast where the host dresses the guests in the family *samurai* clothes and his wife performs a folk dance. Such experiences remain fixed in the memory.

Having travelled quite widely in Japan at intervals over three decades, I am reasonably conversant in the ritual of the house and toilet slippers, the etiquette of the bath and so on. Thus, the following episode could hardly be excused on the grounds of ignorance or lack of experience. What I can say in my own defence is that, my legs no longer having the strength and resilience of youth, certain actions are performed with some difficulty. So that is the reason, if not the excuse, for a matter of some embarrassment which I will relate in due course.

Some *minshuku* are so deep in the country that the *o-tearai* (perhaps, more accurately, the *o-benjo*) consists merely of a round hole in the floor with a cesspit beneath. On one occasion, I accidentally flipped a toilet slipper irretrievably into the noisome depths. Showing commendable strength of character, I resisted the temptation to dispatch its mate to the same fate, so the proprietor was no doubt puzzled to find an uneven number of toilet slippers inside the door. But, I digress.

This story concerns a *minshuku* located at a hot spring a mile or two from the main town on Sado Island. Being a modern, white-painted concrete structure of no architectural merit, it lacked the charm of those situated in old houses as, say, the *gasshô-zukuri* dwellings of Shirakawa-go or the former *geisha* houses of Kanazawa. It was managed by a family I shall call the Yamamuras, who clearly took great pride in their establishment. Everything in their domain was spotlessly clean, neat and tidy, for they ran a tight ship, so to speak, with friendly efficiency.

The place was a bit up-market. The corridors, instead of the usual polished wooden boards, were carpeted, and at the entrance to each room there was a small alcove where one could remove one's slippers. In the rooms there were small vases of fresh flowers. The food, and in particular the seafood, was excellent and I defy anyone to find more delicious *sashimi* in the best restaurant in Tokyo. Yamamura-san senior was tall, erect and rather thin. Although his demeanour was on the serious side, he was politeness itself. He went beyond the call of duty to make his guests comfortable.

For my edification Yamamura-san senior found a sort of English translation of the information sheet provided for the guests. Of course, the usual rule banning firearms and swords was included. Guests were also warned against 'twisting, distorting or otherwise changing the shape of the facilities'. In case of earthquakes guests could be secure in the knowledge that if they 'obey the instructions we will be a worker'. One of the listed attractions was the 'exciting night-life of Sado Island', available on TV at a cost of 100 yen per ten minutes. This turned out to be — not singing in *karaoke* bars or Okesa folkdancing — but a porn channel of no discernible regional significance, and of impenetrable coyness. The plot was very simple, but just as the action showed signs of becoming interesting the screen dissolved into a mosaic of little coloured squares like an animated cubist painting. The mystery of the Japanese censors' mindset is beyond the understanding of mere mortals. There was, however, a positive aspect — my comprehension level of the Japanese language sound-track shot to unprecedented heights. Perhaps this could be attributed to the fact that the dialogue, or rather the monologue, consisted mainly of feminine ooohs, aaahs, ohhhs and (presumably) orgasmic squeals.

At this point, gentle reader, I should warn that the following scenes might offend. Still with me? Then please read on.

Yamamura-san's *o-tearai* was as spotless as the rest of the premises. The white tiled floor gleamed, the plumbing fixtures shone and all the requirements of that lowly but necessary side of life were provided. The toilet bowls consisted of the usual white porcelain trough with a hood at one end, set into the tiled floor. The squatting posture is said to be healthy, and for those born to it no doubt it is, but for a rather mature *gaijin* considerable stress is inflicted on will and muscles. With the added complication of a stiff knee, I found it helpful to grasp the flush pipe for support. This placed my body at a slight angle to the line of the trough and, rather like a pilot landing his plane on a narrow airstrip in a crosswind, an extra measure of skill and judgement was called for.

When returning to my room on one occasion, I was gratified to find that whereas my slippers usually fell off my feet at every step, I was making better progress than expected. However, after removing my slippers in the entrance alcove it was fortunate that I did not step onto the tatami-matted floor, because the reason for my newfound slipper skill soon became obvious — my left slipper was held to my heel by a small amount of an unmistakable soft brown substance.

Panic! What to do? Clear thinking was required. First things first. I grabbed a towel and soap. Then, holding my slippers and walking on tiptoe, I scurried along the corridor to the communal wash basins and did a quick clean-up job. But there were further ramifications to consider. If I had soiled my house slipper, then one of the toilet slippers must be in the same deplorable condition. I must immediately rush to the toilet, find the offending slipper and clean it. Unfortunately, I was too late. Yamamura-san senior was standing bolt upright by the door and gazing down in horrified disbelief at a brown stain on the blue carpet where I had changed into the house slippers. No Japanese person could have been guilty of such deplorable carelessness. I was the only *gaijin* in the house. There was no escape. '*Gomen nasai*', I blurted out, before my tenuous grasp of the language collapsed. I fled to my room to consult my dictionary and phrasebook. How about '*hazukashii desu*'? One authority declared that it meant 'I am embarrassed' but the other said 'I am ashamed'. I was embarrassed alright but not ashamed. However, this was hardly the time for fine semantic distinctions. I shuffled off to look for Yamamura-san senior, passing on the way a maid sponging the carpet. He was at the front desk. '*Hazukashii desu*', I said, and added for good measure, '*Jiko deshita*', even though it was clearly an accident. Of course, it was only my guilty conscience that made his demeanour seem a little more distant than usual and his bow slightly more perfunctory. Ever polite, he said something to the effect that it didn't matter. Perhaps he blamed himself for allowing a foreigner into his house.

The next morning, the spot had completely disappeared — but that mark can never be expunged from my memory. Yamamura-san senior greeted me as if nothing untoward had happened. He drove me to the bus station and insisted that I phone him when I returned from a trip to the other side of the island so that he could pick me up.

Dear reader, there is a moral to be drawn from this sorry tale: when travelling in Japan do take care not to put your foot in it!

Gentlemen Prefer Plum Wine

David Myers

'Unfortunately no ladies allow', proclaimed Pepsi-Kola-san. He beamed happily. 'Secretary Mrs Hashishowa prefer urgently return home. Ah, Japanese lady enjoy to clean house.'

Secretary Mrs Hashishowa was silent as she chauffeured the four men in her brand new imperial blue Cedric. She most certainly did not prefer returning home. But it would be unthinkable to complain. Her face was carefully composed to express nothing.

Dean Anthony St Clair, being a mere Australian, could not understand. Why couldn't Mrs Hashishowa come to dinner too? Surely it would be more fun to have a pretty woman come to the party. He sadly waved good-bye to her as the four men turned to enter an inauspicious house with no identifying sign. Pepsi-Kola-san frowned. Silly *gaijin* does not understand Japanese custom, he thought to himself. No manners.

The men followed a *geisha* girl in elaborate *kimono* along a pathway of grey, granite stepping stones. There was no sign of a kitchen or indeed of other guests in this totally silent restaurant. The procession observed a respectful silence. This is more like a funeral procession than a dinner party, thought Anthony.

The thick *kimono* enveloped the beautiful *geisha* girl from head to foot. Every female curve was decently flattened out and enshrouded in delicate secrecy. Not a hint of coquettishness or saucy feminine allure could be detected. She was like an Egyptian mummy brought back to life. She minced along in tiny steps in her clumsy wooden sandals with her eyes cast downwards as required.

Her *kimono* was her adornment, but it was also her prison. The *kimono* restricted her walking. She was like a hobbled horse: easy to catch and easy to tame. But the Japanese gentlemen made no indecent gestures. There was no vulgar horseplay. Their decorum was irreproachable.

The gentlemen sat formally on their floor cushions around a low coffee table. New *geisha* girls at either end of the coffee table knelt on the *tatami* floor and bowed respectfully and repeatedly. One was old and ugly and one was young and beautiful. Both exhibited perfect self-discipline. Dean St Clair admired their posture and wondered about the muscles in their knees and their backs. He himself sprawled helplessly on the straw floor, all legs, elbows and awkwardness.

'Now relax!' commanded Pepsi-Kola-san.

No one twitched a muscle. No one was going to fall for that piece of nonsense and be the first fool to break the spell of the ceremony. The silence had become almost religious. Everyone knew that relaxing was out of the question. The name of the game was dignity in order to show each other respect. There were decencies to be observed and rituals to be executed.

Simultaneously, the old *geisha* at one end of the table and the young *geisha* at the other end, both still kneeling and bowing, poured bubbling Kirin beer into the minuscule glasses. Professor Hongobashi was the senior member of the party. His eyes expressed sixty-five years of sensitivity, self-restraint and a profound experience of human squabbling and greed. He permitted himself the merest hint of an ironic twinkle as he raised his minute beer glass. Nodding his head courteously, he pronounced *'Kampai!'*. The gentlemen raised their glasses in salute and drank.

God, is this ever going to be bor–ing, thought Dean St Clair. He knew already what was coming. About fifty minuscule courses of unidentifiable particles of fish presented in exquisite arrangements over a period of four hours and washed down with increasing quantities of liquor.

The sliding bamboo and opaque paper walls operated soundlessly and the *geisha* girls shuffled and bowed, in and out, in and out. The minute beer glasses became a discreet battlefield between the drinkers and the *geisha* girls. The drinkers were determined to empty the glasses. The girls were more determined to keep the glasses filled to the very top.

An hour passed. The gentlemen discarded their jackets. Dr Tsutsukitsu's face had become a deep, shiny red. He jabbered away with ferocity, stabbing his finger in the air to emphasise his points. Pepsi-Kola-san translated:

'This very serious philosophy. He say: "What you think of Japanese tradition and how is Australian different from American in this respect?". I tell him in Australia your wife is boss. This is correct, okay? I have seen myself. But Japanese gentlemen have freedom. Wife stay home. Prefer make beautiful and clean house. This is best system.'

Dean St Clair smiled nervously. The situation required diplomacy. He was after all outnumbered and an honoured guest. He thought ruefully that back in Australia he was generally considered to be a conservative fossil and a male chauvinist of the old school. Here in Japan he was clearly regarded as an incompetent or even impotent male who didn't know how to discipline women or control his own wife. He really must stop telling Pepsi-Kola-san about his spectacular fights with his wife, Natasja. Clearly, Pepsi-Kola-san misunderstood both the rights of Australian wives and the intellectual fascination of Dean St Clair in studying the causes of these fights.

'I like mixed dinner parties', he answered Dr Tsutsukitsu. And left it at that.

'This is mixed dinner party', chimed in Professor Hongobashi, who was beginning to look decidedly jovial, if not downright mischievous. 'Two *geisha* girls are good mixed. You want more maybe? You greedy?'

'Time for plum wine', proclaimed Pepsi-Kola-san. 'Then singing.'

The plum wine was as potent as it was chilled. The gentlemen blinked happily at each other and with increasing vagueness. They even poured beer for the two *geisha* girls, who were still kneeling in perfect decorum. The *geisha* girls were careful to strike a delicate balance between sipping at the beer and not actually drinking any of it.

'Japanese women stay home. Japanese men travel', persisted Dr Tsutsukitsu. He was like a dog gnawing on a bone. He might go on for hours.

'I travel', said the pretty *geisha* girl in a Tinkerbell voice. 'I travel to Syd-cnny, Kings'o Crosso and also the Goldo Coasto.'

Dean St Clair opened his mouth like a stunned mullet. He was astounded. The *geisha* girl had spoken. She had taken part in the ritual without permission. Would she be struck down with lightning or would one of the gentlemen cut off her head with a ceremonial officer's sword?

Dr Tsutsukitsu fell off his chair laughing.

'New fashion Japanese girl', he giggled. '*Shinjinrui*. Very bad. Tellible.'

The *geisha* girl did not look in the slightest new-fashioned. Anthony wondered if she had worn her *kimono* to Kings'o Crosso and was her visit for pleasure, for business or for a honeymoon. Certainly, the *geisha* girl, having spoken, now gave no sign of being about to jump out of her corsets and lay waste the countryside with a lecture on women's liberation or feminism. Nevertheless, the fact remained that she had spoken. She was human after all. Dean St Clair toasted her health stealthily and wondered lecherously what she was like under the *kimono*.

But Dr Tsutsukitsu got up off his floor cushion and began to dance. By himself. He saw no need for a female partner for this dance. It was after all his dance.

'This is how we dance on Fukue Island', he yelled, and hopped and skipped around the straw *tatami* mat like a grizzly bear with fire in his belly and lead boots on his feet. It was lucky that he was short and thick-set with a low centre of gravity. He swayed uncertainly in dangerous proximity to the coffee table covered with delicate dishes and drinks.

'*Hai, hai! Omedetô!*' roared Professor Hongobashi. 'Congratulations!'

To his considerable surprise, Dean St Clair found that he was dancing with Dr Tsutsukitsu. The *geisha* girls applauded. Pepsi-Kola-san took a large number of indiscreet photos.

'England–Australia has no Emperor. Has Queen', pronounced Professor Hongobashi with the certainty of absolute knowledge. He beamed. 'God save our gracious Queen!' he sang. And sang every word right to the end while waving his hands like a conductor. He was clearly an Anglophile. 'I English gentleman', he said. Then he clapped himself.

'Could the Queen of England come to our gentleman's evening?' Dean St Clair's voice was carefully polite but had an unmistakably ironic edge. He looked Professor Hongobashi in the face, culture to culture, man to man, eyeball to eyeball. 'The Queen of England is a woman, isn't she?'

Professor Hongobashi looked at Anthony as though he were an amiable but pitiful moron. 'Of course woman', he replied courteously. He wondered whether the honourable *gaijin* was a bit thick.

'Of course woman', he repeated and smiled. 'But for tonight we make an honorary man.'

He roared with laughter at his effortless victory in logic. Pepsi-Kola-san also applauded this example of Japanese lateral thinking. Small wonder that with innovative thinking like this they were the leading industrial nation in the world.

Dr Tsutsukitsu had stopped dancing. He resumed his seat, his face shining a deep maroon with plum wine, happiness and honest exertion.

'I read book about Japanese submarine in Syd-enny Harbour', he said, apropos of nothing in particular. 'Brave men. No ladies.' His logical connection became a little less obscure. 'Japanese ladies stay home prefer house cleaning.' He looked triumphant.

Dean St Clair remembered as a child climbing secretly onto the Japanese mini-submarine on exhibition in the Canberra war museum. It had been a grisly feeling. A suicide mission of sailors dedicating their lives to the Emperor. A ferry had been sunk in the harbour. None of the Australian warships had been touched. Nothing much more, except terror. And lots of wild rumours at the time. A Japanese invasion seemed imminent.

Dean St Clair wondered what response was required of him by Australian national honour. Should he scream abuse at Japanese war-mongers and a power-hungry Emperor? Should he express outrage that peaceful Sydney Harbour should be invaded by sneaky Japanese submarines? But then, seen historically, would he not have to express equal outrage at the Australian invasion of Turkey in 1916 or of Vietnam in the 1960s? And what about the arrogance of Commodore Perry towards Japan in 1854?

Was Nietzsche right after all? Were all human beings driven by a lust for power and did only the weak take refuge in the hypocritical Christian morality of egalitarianism and pacifism? Morality was for failures and power for the victors.

'Australian soldiers, Japanese soldiers, all brave', he finally responded, after what may have been minutes but was probably only long seconds. He wondered if the Australian RSL would be satisfied with this response. Perhaps in a show of virile patriotism he should have challenged Dr Tsutsukitsu to a *kendô* duel.

To his amazement he actually heard himself saying, '*Kendô!*'. Perhaps he was a chauvinist after all. It must be the plum wine. It brought out the warrior in him.

'*Kendô*, no *kendô!*' grinned Pepsi-Kola-san. 'Only *kendô* tonight gentleman aim at *geisha* girl.'

And he poked his finger playfully at the *geisha*. The girl laughed respectfully. Pepsi-Kola-san laughed with deep satisfaction. He was the host and this was a number one gentleman's night. The *gaijin* was providing some unexpected amusement.

By now all four men were thoroughly pleased with themselves. Self-doubt and problems had been washed away by the chilled plum wine. They clinked glasses amiably and drank a ceremonial *kampai* again.

Professor Hongobashi discovered that Dean St Clair spoke German. In quivering, lugubriosi style they sang together: '*Da draussen vor dem Tore/ Da steht ein Lindenbaum*'. They wiped tears of satisfying melancholy from their eyes. They day-dreamed of their student days in Germany and their lost youth and the elusive peace that was promised to them in the shade of the Lindenbaum.

The *geisha* girls wiped their eyes too in a display of social sympathy. They were like a well-trained chorus on the stage. It was their duty to provide feminine back-up support to the main players. The main players were born hams.

Gradually Professor Hongobashi took over the role of acting as the evening's intellectual trend setter. Dr Tsutsukitsu had lapsed into a narcissistic reverie of military glory in which he was a submarine captain approaching Sydney Harbour.

'Periscope up!' he muttered to himself. 'Prepare torpedo for launching!' He made appropriate noises that sounded like 'Bzz Brm Brm'. He was as absorbed as a baby in a sandpit. '*Banzai!*' No one was listening although the *geisha* girls pretended to occasionally.

Professor Hongobashi might be a slow starter, but he was clearly now into his second wind. In fact he showed signs of becoming unstoppable. He burst into a rousing rendition of Beethoven's Ninth Symphony, ' Ode to Joy'.

'Alle Menschen werden Brüder', he sang.

'Wo Dein sanfter Flügel weilt', gargled Dean St Clair.

They drank to being brothers and to Schiller's angel of peace and joy. Oddly enough, it seemed that Germany was destined to play the role of restorer of international peace and harmony, on this particular evening anyway.

There are always lots of brothers when you're drunk, thought Anthony. Or he would have thought this, if his mind had been a little clearer. What he actually thought was: Bugger the brothers! Where are the sisters? Not to mention the nieces!

Sisters — in the wider, metaphorical sense of females in general, certainly not females within the family — were so much less bellicose and threatening. They soothed one so. Japanese 'sisters' were especially delicate and refined because they laughed at his jokes, regardless of whether they were funny or not. Dean St Clair loved the way that Japanese girls covered their tiny mouths with their hands while they giggled. He looked at the *geisha* girls and sighed. They sighed back respectfully like a chorus and waited patiently for the next cue.

Pepsi-Kola-san misinterpreted Anthony's sigh as an expression of deep happiness and fulfilment. This was understandable as he himself was feeling very happy and fulfilled. Professor Hongobashi and Dr Tsutsukitsu were his honoured business associates. It was gratifying to be able to provide them with so much happiness and entertainment.

'You see', he explained forgivingly to his friend Dean St Clair, 'for this evening Mrs Hashishowa is not necessary. Maybe tomorrow, for example. Golfing. Tonight is gentlemen's night'.

Professor Hongobashi was away with the fairies conducting the climax to Beethoven's magnificent finale in the Ninth Symphony. There were tears in his eyes. Dr Tsutsukitsu was weaving in his chair whispering 'Brrm Brz Brz'. The *geisha* girls were smiling with genuine happiness. The madam had praised them for pleasing her customers. There would be a big bonus to take home tonight. Japanese gentlemen paid well for pleasing female company with impeccable manners. Everyone was satisfied with the completed ritual.

'Japanese custom is best, I am thinking', said Pepsi-Kola-san. It would have been hard to refute him.

Shizuka

Ian Hamilton

It's time for us to leave Japan now. Two and a half years has been too short.

There's much we'll miss for the rest of our lives; old and doddery on the front porch we'll scan again through our photographs and laugh a little, muse a little, and no doubt wonder what happened to so-and-so even though we truly do mean to keep up with our letters and New Year cards.

Will we ever really get all those photos together in albums, neatly compiled with dates and names, or will they stay forever in their packets, tumbling about in the bottom of the bookcase?

The truth is, we will probably continue for an eternity to ask each other, 'Was it in June or August we did that trip to Wajima? You remember that old man in the *soba* shop, when you asked him about all the thatch roofs, and I worried about the thatch being full of creepy, crawly things? And he said . . .'.

'Oh, yes, I remember! He said they put mice in the roof to keep the insects down and you said *mice*! and he said, no worries, we put a snake in the attic to keep down the mice.'

'You know, he *had* to be having us on, they couldn't . . .'

'Yes, they could.'

Nice houses in Wajima, but none so excellent as our little Tree House at Irita Bay. The sign on the door says *Shizuka*, peace and quiet, and while it's apt it never really stuck with us. It was and always will be our Tree House, high on the lip of a valley and surrounded on three sides by dense forest: white cedar, pines that go rusty in winter and tall stands of bamboo bowing and slow-dancing in the wind, *susuki* (Japanese pampas grass), dogwoods, plums, wild winter jonquils, and a carnival of azaleas in the springtime.

It looks at the moment as though we are going down to Indonesia to live, and that's an excitement, the secretly nervous pleasure of expectation and wondering peppers our conversations; new friends, new sensations, new delights; but of the old ones our Tree House will be the memory most yearned for, the subject most popular when late at night the conversation turns wistfully to, 'Ah, but when we lived in Japan . . .'.

A couple of country kids at heart, the hectic pace and the mad razzle-dazzle of the world's biggest city fast became a drug for us; it swept us up, willing and happy pebbles in a wild avalanche of long days and late neon nights, new restaurants, crazy people and frenzied moments that spiked our drinks and took us on to new Tokyo highs.

But on the weekends we needed space.

We found our space at the end of the Izu Peninsula, that seismic and shaky stretch of Cipango that hangs like a teardrop 200 kilometres south of Tokyo.

Mostly we drove down late Friday night at the end of another mad week. Home late from work, eat lightly, no booze just coffee, then hit the truckie's drag track on the Tomei Expressway, a race through the night, through the tollgates with our correct toll ready, down to Odawara and along the spectacular Emerald Coast through the glitter city of Atami, and Ito, finally over the mermaid bridge and through Shimoda and up, further up into the dark hills above Iritahama, the road narrowing, with tangy *amanatsu*, that fruit somewhere between an orange and a grapefruit, hanging over the car.

Up again, lugging our bags of casual clothes and a couple of bottles of wine up the steep stone steps and, at last, after three hours of travelling and always with a sigh of happiness, the sense of coming home: our Tree House.

The living room and kitchen area paved with stone and timber, the ceiling held up with rough logs, a couple of *tatami* rooms for sleeping — one for us, one for the rare lucky guests — *tatami*, the flooring of rice straw tightly woven together with reeds which feels more natural to walk on or sleep on in any season than the most expensive carpet or mattress. But always our first thought, after turning on the gas and checking the toilet for spiders, was for the wide balcony, our real space, which looked out over the sleepy valley, the lights of the little village snug below, and across to the Pacific Ocean silver under the moon and the bright, measured flashes of the Tower of Lightning.

Hisako-san, our dearest friend with her halting English, named it that way the night she helped us find our Tree House, and it never ever could be a lighthouse after that, always the Tower of Lightning.

Hisako-san! To find our Tree House we stayed a week in the small cabin of an acquaintance and we visited the *Nôkyô*, the farmer's co-operative, to see if they had our space for us.

Nakamura-san, a most elegant and charming woman, gave us her total attention and hours of her time, but we kept pointing up into the green hills; Up There, we kept saying, and she had nothing.

Either on a whim or more likely a message from the gods, she introduced us to Mr and Mrs Toraya, proud of their little 'motel', a string of *tatami* rooms with little kitchenettes, and a splendid *o-furo*, nearly big and opulent enough for the entire village to bathe in. Mrs Toraya, tiny and jolly, always smiling, made a quick phone call and then tea, and Mr Toraya sat with us at an outside table and fiddled with a metal bracket he was repairing. He looked very serious and he nodded, '*Hai . . . hai . . . hai*', as Nakamura-san explained our difficulty.

The Toraya-sans' mutt Rocky sniffed at our foreign ankles then curled up at our feet to make us feel at home.

Rocky died of old age a year later and we felt his owners' loss.

How little you know of future events when they begin so innocently: while we never saw Nakamura-san again, these two good people were soon to become our Mama-san and Papa-san, our landlady and landlord, our friends and our drinking mates.

A tiny van drove up and a pleasant young Japanese woman joined us, introducing herself as Hisako. She explained that she had a hairdressing salon and beauty shop in the village and that she had done her training in, of all places, San Antonio, Texas. When she first came to Iritahama she lived with the Toraya-sans; she treated them as she would treat her own parents.

We sat like a couple at the tennis, heads swivelling from one side of the table to the other, trying to follow the conversation.

Finally Hisako-san told us, 'Do not worry now. Papa-san knows everybody. He knows already what you need. He will find it. They have asked you to come tonight for alcohol and snacks and we will talk more'.

We returned some hours later, burned from the beach at Kisamiohama, more accurately Kisami Bay but known to all the locals, we discovered, as 'Ohama Beachie', where the surf was just like home but the water was unfamiliarly clean, as clean as you could buy in a bottle.

How many glorious summer days did we spend on that beach, under our 'beachie parasol'?

Mrs Toraya made it quite clear to us that nothing further would happen until we had properly sampled their *o-furo*. When we emerged later, like a couple of ripe tomatoes, Hisako-san had arrived and Mr Toraya had removed the stopper from the big bottle of *sake* we had brought as a gift and now he was worrying over the charcoal in his barbecue.

The conversation, in English, Japanese, Japlish, body language, hand signals and a little dance and mime, ranged over our life stories.

Mr Toraya had grown up on one of the Izu Islands and he still prided himself on his ability to body surf, a claim that sent Mrs Toraya into howls of gently derisive laughter.

We had to explain about Ayers Rock and the Gold Coast and whether kangaroos were very friendly.

Not once did we talk about our dream, our *bessô*, our weekend house that waited for us somewhere in the darkening hills.

When we had destroyed the *sake* and the whisky and all the beer, plus a platter of *sashimi* nearly as big as the table, sea urchin, boiled peanuts, grilled lobster and shrimp, salad with cress and bean sprouts and onions and seaweed, then ice cream, we were allowed to go home to rest.

Though not for too long. The breakfast dishes were still in the sink when Hisako-san and Mr and Mrs Toraya came tapping on the door of our borrowed cabin, their faces bright and eager in the early light, ready to show us some houses in the hills.

There was no mercy for the sick and weary that day. Zipping about in Hisako-san's tiny van, up and down the narrow trails, we inspected a dozen houses for rent but none pleased all five of us perfectly and it was clear that Japanese consensus had taken over: *all* of us must be delighted or *none* of us could be.

Mr and Mrs Toraya went home for a serious conference on the matter while Hisako-san bought us a *bentô* each and walked us down a jungle track to a secret open-air rock pool few knew about, where we sat in the steaming spring water, ate our *sushi*, looked across Suruga Bay to Mt Fuji in the distance, and learned to love our new friend.

Our hangovers had gone but still we agreed with each other on an early night. Yet the moment we pulled the *futons* from the cupboard there they were again, excitedly banging on the door, so pleased with themselves they could barely speak.

Back into the van and up, way up now, into the dark forest and up the stone steps and there it was, our Tree House, just as we had all imagined it would be and it was ours for the next two years, in a quiet cul-de-sac where we seldom saw another soul except the birds, the odd stray cat dropping by to cadge a meal and a cuddle, and the Toraya-sans and Hisako-san.

Shizuka, indeed, was our Tree House.

Ah, those photographs and memories, of the first night we invited them for dinner. Mr Toraya struggled up the steps with his little barbecue and showed us how to light Japanese charcoal. He cooked shrimp. We cooked chicken legs marinated in soy and honey and chilli and garlic.

Mrs Toraya showed us how to use the rice cooker.

We toasted each other in *sake* and wine and beer and scotch.

We gave Mr Toraya the first big cigar of his life and he insisted on being photographed with it. Then he burst into song, joined softly by Mrs Toraya, a song with all the mystery of a legend yet it was a true story of the first woman in the area to become the discarded lover of a foreigner, America's first consul to Japan who lived some years not far from here before the Meiji government would allow him to approach Tokyo.

Then we sang our own songs, silly songs from childhood; it didn't matter, the songs clearly pleased.

Hisako-san sang a song she'd learned in Texas.

From our balcony in daylight we watched the kites who nested in the headlands soar over the valley; in the spring we watched two kites in love dive-bombing each other for hours in the thermals; we could almost hear their laughter and we certainly shared their joy.

Late summer, the swifts migrating south from Siberia entertained us, feeding on the wing in the late afternoons as the insects rose from the forest floor, putting on an aerial display more spectacular than the Spitfires over London.

Chirruping resident bulbuls chased each other through the treetops. Tiny brown warblers serenaded us summer mornings, and little green willow warblers blew in through winter from the Izu Islands.

Finches and starlings dropped by. For several weeks one autumn, a pygmy woodpecker no bigger than a man's thumb made machine gun noises outside our bedroom window at dawn, hammering into the trees for termites; it was only on our third weekend we finally identified where the sound was coming from and then we ceased cursing it and rolled over and went back to sleep.

A family of glossy black jungle crows with high domed heads, far bigger than the Australian crow, claimed the valley as their territory and they were in a constant state of war with the kites.

Once, a kite floated lazily over our house, a couple of metres above our heads, one sharp eye checking us out, and from out of the sun flew the Hun with the gun; a fiercely angry crow, claws extended, slammed onto the back of the kite, and the kite squealed in pain and left hurriedly, but was back within a few minutes, defiantly seeking lunch.

One winter weekend five crows set upon one of the kites. The kite flew higher and higher towards the heavens until we could barely see it and only one crow remained, darting furiously from below; then the kite abruptly flipped over, folded his wings, and slammed hard into the shocked crow, sending him back down to the lower altitudes where he belonged instead of pretending he could fly high with the big boys.

We hated having to stay in Tokyo the following weekend, reckoning we would miss Round Two.

Oh, and the food.

The live lobsters we bought from a man on the beach at Yumigahama and barbecued in the sunset.

Senda, the little Japanese restaurant smack in the middle of the paddy fields where, as the rice grew green, the *tsuru*, Japanese cranes, would promenade in stately arrogance and then, when the sun went down and we could no longer see them, we sat on Senda's tatami floor and ate their *teishoku*, a selection of their very best lobster and sashimi and *chawan-mushi*, that wondrous savoury custard hiding morsels of crab and tangy mushrooms, washed down with barley tea. The old lady at Senda always welcomed us with a huge country smile and the farmers and their families nodded politely as if we had become locals at last.

Sunnyside, on the beach at Kisamiohama, where Saito-san makes the best bacon and cheese pizza outside Italy, a genuine pizza this one and quite properly it takes a while to prepare, none of your factory variety here, and we could sit for hours and play backgammon if we wished, or borrow a pack of cards, or just sit, and sit, and sit and maybe watch the *sumo* on television, no frantic rush to 'turn the tables over' in this place: Saito-san's hours are as flexible as his customers wish them to be and if the fishing's lively he's unlikely to open until he's good and ready. But he's just as relaxed about closing time.

Hisako-san showed us Sukushi, where we sat around the edges of the old fishing boat filled with water and good live things to eat, sometimes secretly dropping a little morsel in for a crab to nibble, trying to forget for a moment that we might well be cleaning out his carapace ourselves shortly.

And the *sushiya,* where three generations of the family pleased us, father and son making *sushi*, mother or daughter bringing tea with granddaughter on the hip, or crawling around us gooing at us bright-eyed from behind the counter.

We talked about dropping out and living in the Tree House forever, one of us making string bags to sell by the roadside until it was pointed out to him that he still has trouble tying his shoelaces correctly. Maybe *amanatsu* marmalade would catch on . . . ?

Very soon now they'll be calling our flight, all aboard to somewhere.

Two and a half years has not been long enough. We would have happily stretched that by at least a decade.

Hospitality Challenge Japan

Tony Barrell

*G*etting lost in Australia is serious. You can die a hideous, lonely death stranded in dangerous wilderness. In Japan you can be lost in the crowd, be submerged to the point of panic by the swirling strangeness of dense alien culture, especially if you don't read Japanese; but even in the most baffling tumult there are guardian angels waiting to assist. In fact, you can't get lost in Japan even if you try. Sooner or later, someone will track you down; not only will they tell you where you are, they'll tell you where you should be and then they'll take you there whether you like it or not. But despite the help and friendliness, you get the feeling you'll always be lost.

We're on a neck of land waiting for a bus that might not come, looking for an explanation for something that's obvious to everyone except us: the woman with the twelve children.

Once you get to Shodoshima there are no signs in *romaji*, the roman alphabet version of Japanese, so if you don't read *kanji* or *kana* you are lost. Shodoshima is a small island off the northeast coast of Shikoku, the smallest of Japan's large islands. It's a ferry ride from the Shikoku port of Takamatsu or you can come direct from Kobe, Osaka or Okayama on the main Japanese island of Honshu. The only people who wander Shodoshima in winter are Shingon Buddhist pilgrims — *henro* — usually in coach parties, sometimes alone but rarely on foot. Shodoshima has a user-friendly miniature version of the much more arduous eighty-eight temple trek around Shikoku. Devout *henro* do Shodoshima as a wind-down from the big pilgrimage; the less pious take it as the easy option.

I'm writing a play about an old *kabuki* actor who did it on foot and then jumped to his death from a ferryboat on the way back to Kobe. I want to see his last landscape, a temple to Kannon, but we've been distracted by the mysterious woman with the twelve children. She's on public plaques, podiums, posters and plinths; they can't be her offspring because they're all the same age. There's no mention of them in the English guidebooks but our *kanji*-only map shows some kind of tourist attraction in a village at the tip of the cape. Our homage hasn't been well planned. We've been walking along the coast road for an hour but no bus has passed in either direction. There are stops signs but no timetables.

'What are you doing here?'

It's Mr O, bowlegged, in half-framed horn-rims and a three-piece, pinstriped, dark blue suit under an open over-coat, and Mrs O, whose frames have silver-studded wingtips. She has a tight greying perm and a green woollen coat with an artificial fur collar. Both are walking briskly towards us, as if they knew we were coming. They're in their late sixties.

'*Onna to tomodachi*', I mumble. There's a silent moment as he extracts sense from my crippled pronunciation, then he nods and sucks air through his clenched teeth. I assume they will walk on, so I look away from them, down at the bay where an old ferry is keeling over in the shallows, its cream and green superstructure streaked red and dusty with rust. Mr O follows our gaze and proudly says the tub belongs to him. To tell foreign strangers you own a wreck seems a strange boast, but Mr O explains he recycles old boats. Next week his men will tear it apart, stack it and wrap it until every plate is severed, slivered and shaved for retrieval by an Osaka steel mill.

It's nice to know, but the day is beginning to die and we need guidance.

'*Tabemono*', I say. Food. It's crude but serviceable communication only slightly more polite than pointing to my open mouth.

Mr O beckons, turns and walks quickly down the road and then suddenly sweeps left, and heads across the isthmus. Mrs O waits a moment, then sets off after him and turns to beckon that we follow. We move faster than we've done all day, downhill through a narrow lane, between houses and towards the water. We reach a pebble beach spread with nets and then stride to a sudden stop in front of a house. We are lost but we're home. It's an inn, secret, without a sign.

We duck and smile, remove our shoes, and sit in a spacious *tatami*-matted dining room with sliding glass doors overlooking a carp pond, rocks and *bonsai* firs. It's warm enough, but the landlady turns up an electric heater, then listens dutifully while Mr O firmly instructs her to bring us lunch. A phone call is made and a butcher's boy brings large and lumpy steaks, which the landlady cooks with chips. It's the first time we haven't eaten Japanese in three weeks. While we struggle through it, Mr and Mrs O quietly drink tea at a separate table. At the end of the meal there's no possibility of our paying. Mr O shakes his head so dismissively we don't even try.

Mr and Mrs O then join us and we draw maps on the paper tablecloth and talk about the weather and the woman with the twelve children.

It seems she's Miss K from the fifties novel *Twenty-four Eyes*, by Sakae Tsuboi, the tale of a village school-teacher in the years before the war.

'The film', says Mrs O, 'was made here a long time ago'. The film provides the images for the statues and calendars we've been seeing ever since we arrived.

'In 1953', says Mrs O.

Mr O asks which part of the States we are from.

'We are from Australia', says Teri's mother. This makes things very different. Mrs O has friends in Bendigo and is soon to visit them.

'Australia, good', says Mr O. It is the last word; it explains everything. America is important, Japan is home, but Australia is all right.

He pays the bill and makes a phone call. In minutes a taxi arrives. The driver, a handsome, tall, grey-haired man with a moustache and aviator Raybans gets out and shakes hands. He speaks some English. While Mr O stays behind to manage his business, the driver and Mrs O show us the Museum of Twenty-four Eyes, an old, low, wooden school house, its rooms rimmed with production stills from the film. We've never seen it, or read the book, so it's impossible to decide whether the display is authentic or not. Mrs O's look says: we could have told you it was not for foreigners, but never mind.

Outside we take a photograph of Mrs O, then the cab takes us back to the main road where we sit and wait for the bus. Mr O has already paid the fare.

We bump around on the bus for half an hour before anyone speaks.

'Do you remember the man at Shinjuku?' says Teri. Deep in the subway labyrinth, underneath a clock, we'd been helped by the same man on two separate occasions a week apart. Even though we had had a good map and were getting the hang of finding the route, he had insisted on taking us to our platform.

'Do you think they want us to *stay* lost?' We laugh, but it's serious.

We move on to Kyoto, to view major temples. Our base is a cosy farm *minshuku*, northwest of the city near a huge frozen pond. Bamboo groves start immediately behind the house, and when the wind gets up in the night we hear the 'tack tack' of the trunks. Beyond the groves are foothills and then wild mountains.

We take the local bus to the Daikoku-ji and Ryoan-ji temples. Ryoan-ji has the famous cosmic stone garden; a flutter of snow has flaked the gravel, the *Zen* map has acquired a dripping fringe of icicles. We skid around the verandah in freezing socks. At Daikoku-ji it's snowing again, but a monk is dealing with a trader who has a trolley stacked with straw hats and parasols.

'*Ohayô gozaimasu*', I say, a polite morning greeting. The monk replies in rapid Japanese. I grin and shrug, failing to understand anything but the very last syllable '*ka*' which means he's asked me a question.

'*Wakarimasen*', I admit. He mimes puzzlement. His eyes pop, his brow wrinkles in deep ironic furrows, he shakes his head and explodes with mock disbelief.

'I thought you must be Japanese', he says in flawless American.

He buys three hats and waves the trader on his way.

'You understand Japan?' he asks Teri.

'I love it.'

'Of course you do', he says, 'it's easy to understand Japan. But remember, the more you go the less you know', and as he turns away, he grasps his woolly cloak with gloved hands, and pulls it around his heavy silk robe.

'He wears socks and sandals', says Teri, 'does that mean he's English?'. His feet scrunch the gravel. We feel we've seen a slit in the wall of *Zen*.

Aside from a pair of Canadian hiker-pilgrims who rise very early, we are the only foreigners in the *minshuku*. It's crammed with crammers, young final-year high school students from all over Japan who are sitting entrance examinations at Kyoto universities, studying all night, and going off to the college in the morning to take part in their final scholastic hell.

Next to the main dining room there's a cosier, warmer *tatami* zone with a heated *kotatsu*, a low table with a single bar electric heater beneath. We stuff our creaky legs under the quilts and pad the vents to keep in the warmth.

Over Sunday night dinner, the students try their English; friendly, curious, but distracted, their minds on the horrors of Monday. As soon as the spread is eaten and cleared they make moves upstairs for a last hack at the facts.

Or they try.

Enter a tough looking middle-aged exec, Ken from Mitsubeni, who turns the stilted but easy chatter into an international exchange forum. We are bone-weary and want to hit the *tatami*, but Ken tells the boys they must stay downstairs and 'entertain' us. He spits and puffs the words, like a sergeant major from the Kwantung Army bullying a squad of shapeless rookies. We are national 'guests', and conversation with us will be good for their English, and good for mutual co-operation, trade, discipline and digestion.

Like Mr O, Ken treats the help rough; at four a.m. they have a farm to run, but at midnight tonight they must run the corridors with a constant flow of snacks, beers, tea and even bottles of brandy.

After a while we pull what *gaijin* rank we have and insist that Teri is tired and that the boys need to work. Ken takes their shambling exit as a cue to reveal the discreet hates of the *sarariman*. The world economy is stuffed. His company is doomed. It isn't the drink talking. While we've been gagging on potent *shôchû*, Ken's been skolling weak green tea.

Finally, he taps the *tatami*, bends forward, pushes his face until his nose meets the straw, and sniffs in a long and dramatic pull of air.

'Smell that', he says, 'that's Japan', and crisply slaps the mat with the flat of his hand. We've been told and we go to bed.

Takayama is stuffed with tour buses. Parties of middle-aged tourists roll up and down the Edo streets, pausing at the dark old breweries. In the porch of every one there's a complimentary keg of *sake* with cup and ladle, and a message from the owner to 'enjoy'.

We're staying at a huge *minshuku* built in the thirties as some kind of hostel. The other guests are two extended families headed by two seventy-year-old couples, with their sisters, sons and daughters, and grandchildren. They're farmers from Sendai, north of Tokyo. At breakfast the men toast us with *sake*.

They watch us eat fish and nudge each other. They're convinced we're only being polite. It's some kind of salmon with a thick, subtle, delicious sauce. They guffaw when rice falls off our chopsticks. Everything we do is watched closely in open-mouthed amazement by old and young alike.

Mama-san suspects our appetite may be forced by deference, that we'd rather be in a motel.

'You want ham and eggs?'

'No thanks', we insist, 'fish is fine'. The men slap their thighs and chuckle. Nobody believes us.

'I'd like some toast', says Teri.

The bread is thick as a book, soggy with salty butter, delicious.

That night at dinner two of the older men have been sampling free *sake* all day. The one next to me wants me to catch up, and fills my cup. I modestly sip and say, *'Kampai'*. This is not enough. He wants me to down it in one draught so he can fill it again — and again — to show me I can't take it. This I already know, but that's not the point.

'Drink up Australia!' he shouts and the entire room explodes with laughter. He tries to force more into my cup, which is already full to the brim. He stares contemptuously at my abstemiousness and then starts to sing. It's not a solo performance by a man too far into his cups, but a cue for everyone; at the other tables glowing faces join in, drunk, sober, adult and child all singing. Eyes glisten around the room and when the song is over everyone looks towards us; kids have their hands ready to clap. They all want to hear 'Waltzing Matilda'. In the corner Mama-san waits with a loaded tray.

Teri gives me the dark eye.

'Let *them* sing, Dad.' Mama-san knew this was going to happen and scoots in with more drink. Another old farmer takes up the challenge and the whole group is off again on another folk favourite, my turn forgotten, our honour shelved. Only the Japanese can really sing.

Our tiny Tokyo *ryokan* for foreigners near Shinjuku has a sit-up breakfast area with tables topped in red formica and scattered with English language newspapers. The walls are rimmed with photos of flash-dazed guests, grinning next to the hosts, two brothers. 'Excuse me, sir, Mr B, but would you be available at breakfast tomorrow morning at 8.30 a.m.?'

'Yes, we'll be there.'

'Japanese breakfast for all?'

'Yes, that's fine.'

Tokyo is so mild and except for a few essential subway trips we're walking everywhere, energised by so much street exercise we eat everything.

'A television crew will also be available, at breakfast tomorrow. Please, is this okay? You'll be here? 8.30?'

'A TV crew?'

'Yes, special occasion.'

That night we sleep deep and hard on the *tatami* and are slow to move down to the special occasion breakfast. The phone rings.

'You coming down to breakfast now? TV crew ready.'

We sit down to the fish, rice, *miso* soup and side dishes of pickles and rubber. There's no camera crew but we notice lights on stands in each corner of the room and as soon as we start eating the team smoothly moves in, the red light already glowing. The interviewer–director speaks perfect English.

'You like Japanese breakfast?'

'Sure', I reply, pointing at the fish. 'Many people like smoked fish in the morning.' I wonder if I should talk about kippers. He doesn't seem impressed and suddenly brings out a small china bowl of cold dark slime, dark baked beans in glycerine.

'Try this.' He produces a bowl for each of us. The camera moves in to catch our response. The beans glisten in a turbid brew of viscous slime.

'This is *nattô*', says the director, 'fermented soybeans. Tell me what you think'.

I slop some between my sticks, the beans slide down the sauce and plop back into the bowl. I suck in a stream, chew briefly and swallow hard. It looks worse than it tastes and has a faintly beery flavour.

'Traditional Japanese food. You like it?'

'It's —'

'You don't feel ill?'

'No, no, I'm fine, it's —' The truth is what I really feel is of no interest to the crew. They know what they want.

The crew swings on Teri. She bites a bean and grins. Her mother stiffens, rigid white with polite panic she manages a small mouthful. We're not quite what the executive producer ordered — retching *gaijin* clawing at their throats. To make us feel better we each get a corporate pen and a set of cute placemats.

Later, Japanese friends tell me they find *nattô* disgusting but were told as kids that if they didn't eat it, they weren't Japanese.

At Christmas we receive a large glossy photo, the three of us beaming at the *nattô* challenge breakfast. Our segment wasn't used on TV but this very snap is trophied on the *ryokan* wall. We get a three-line note from Mrs O telling us Bendigo was beaut. Next year we get a card thanking us for the photo we took at the school house. We send one more card and then nothing. Duty done all round.

So, when you cut loose from the tour guides, memorise the entrails of Shinjuku and keep what little you already know to yourself. Never pretend you're anything else but deeply and sincerely lost.

Contributors

Susan McAlister Akikusa was born in Sydney and educated in Australia and Europe. She is a journalist specialising in international affairs, and has worked for the print and electronic media in Australia and overseas. She has a BA and MA (International Relations) from the Australian National University. Susan is married to Mitsuru, a Japanese interpreter and business consultant, and they have a daughter, Sarah Yumiko. Susan's hobbies include astronomy and drawing, and from now on, short-story writing competitions.

Tony Barrell was born in Britain and migrated to Australia in 1975. He joined the Australian Broadcasting Corporation in 1976 and has written and produced numerous radio programs about Japan. Tony's long-running pop culture series, 'Nippi Rock Shop', aired on 2JJJ until 1993. He also produced the series 'Japan's Other Voices', and won the Australian Writers' Guild Award in 1989 for his radio drama 'Lost at Sea', which juxtaposed the lives and deaths of *kabuki* actor Ichikawa Danzo and the American lyric poet Hart Crane. Tony has made several visits to Japan, some as a professional, others as a tourist with his family. He is currently working on a book about Japan.

Geoff Bolton juggles corporate life with writing short stories. His work has appeared in *Australian Short Stories*, *The Age Monthly Review* and other small magazines. 'Drawing the Line' is from a yet-unpublished collection of stories, *A Company of Men*, which draws on his experiences working with people in Japanese organisations. Geoff lived in Japan during the 1970s and continues to be interested in Japanese history and culture. He now lives in Sydney.

Anthony Connell spent his childhood in Canberra and Papua New Guinea, after which he found himself bored, grown-up and studying pure mathematics in Queensland. His flatmate at the time was a laser physicist who had spent several years in Japan, and his stories made Japan sound intriguing. Two years later Anthony landed in the Aliens line at Tokyo's Narita Airport, and spent a year working in various jobs in Japan. He finished his degrees in Australia and returned to Japan in 1992 to take up a Daikyo Scholarship at Keio University. Anthony is now a corporate banker in Hong Kong.

Craig J. Dickson studied Japanese as a high school student in Christchurch and spent a year in Yokohama as an exchange student. After graduating from Canterbury University, he returned to Japan for two years on a Monbusho fellowship. Craig then travelled extensively in Europe, got married in Ireland, and worked for several Japanese and Japan-specialist stockbrokers in London before becoming a resident of Japan again in 1991. He works in the credit management section of the Union Bank of Switzerland in Tokyo.

Alan Elliott is a retired director of a small consulting chemistry practice. He first accompanied a friend to Japan on business in the early 1960s, a trip which led to an interest in Japanese arts and crafts. Alan has participated in three '*minshuku* tours' of Japan and has travelled independently in Japan on several occasions, staying in *minshuku*, or inns, whenever possible. Alan is a regular contributor of photographs to the Japanese magazine *Pacific Friend*. 'Japan: A Personal View', an exhibition of his photographs, was held at the Melbourne Camera Club Gallery in 1988.

Ralph Elliott was born in Germany and educated there and in Scotland, where he graduated in English Language and Literature. He served as an officer in the British Army in the Second World War and was severely wounded in action in north-west Europe. Ralph arrived in Australia in 1959, and has taught at three universities. While Master of University House at the Australian National University between 1974 and 1986, he established a staff exchange program and reciprocal membership with Tokyo's International House. Five years ago he was awarded a Japan Society Fellowship for the Promotion of Science, which entailed lecturing at a dozen universities from Tokyo to Kyushu. Ralph is honorary concert manager for the well-known Japanese violinist Miwako Abe.

Frank Foley was born in Ireland and moved with his family to Australia in 1975 at the age of thirteen. He completed a BA (Hons) degree in Asian Studies at Griffith University, which included four years of Japanese language studies. His first visit to Japan was in 1980 as an exchange student. He has now spent over seven years in the country and currently works as manager of a publishing company in Tokyo.

Josie Gibson was born in Stirling, South Australia. After high school, she spent a year as an exchange student in Sapporo, an experience which led to an insatiable interest in Japan, a career as a journalist, an expensive travel bill and stints in the southern United States and London. Josie now lives in Melbourne, where she studies languages at Monash University and works as a journalist for Radio Australia.

Ian Hamilton was born in Melbourne and brought up in places like Bendigo, Mildura, Wagga, Launceston and other Australian towns. His father was an itinerant grocer, and wanderlust runs deep in his family. Ian has worked in advertising in London, New York, Hong Kong, Sydney and Tokyo, where he was the president of Saatchi & Saatchi's Tokyo office. He is the author of several hundred short stories and four mystery novels. Ian is currently drifting around Australia, prior to taking up a job with a Japanese company in Indonesia.

Marie-Jeanne Johnson was born in Toronto, Canada, and moved to Japan in 1990. She is now living in Tokyo, studying, teaching English to four-year-olds, and conducting research for a future thesis on the continuing legends of O-oka Echizen and Toyama no Kin-san in popular culture. Marie was prompted to learn Japanese when her sister, an *anime* fan, took up the language in the 1980s. She now has a special interest of her own — *jidai-geki samurai* TV shows.

John McBride first visited Japan at the age of twelve when he lived on a US army base for two months. Returning to Perth he took up Japanese at high school during the early 1970s. After completing an undergraduate degree at a Japanese university, he worked at the Australia–Japan Foundation in Tokyo. He later graduated from the Australian National University (ANU) and became Executive Officer of the Australia–Japan Research Centre and the Pacific Economic Cooperation Conference Australian Secretariat at the ANU. He is currently working in Tokyo. John is also a licensed tea ceremony teacher and travels to Kyoto regularly for tea ceremonies.

Ben Middleton is currently a PhD student at Cornell University in the United States, specialising in modern Japanese intellectual history. He has lived in Japan for two years, as a high school student and as a student at Keio University. While studying at Keio, he became a great fan of the Tokyo jazz scene. Ben is also very interested in other forms of contemporary popular culture in Tokyo, especially avant-garde theatre.

David Myers is a professor of comparative literature and managing director of the Thailand–Australia Foundation at the University of Central Queensland. He has made over a dozen visits to Japan in the last five years and has helped more than sixty-five Japanese students come to Queensland to study. David is the co-author of *Beyond the Koalas and the Cherry Blossoms*, a book of comical miscommunications between Japanese and Australian people, published in Japanese. He lives with his wife and four children on a mango farm north of Rockhampton.

Hilary Rumley was born in Britain and studied at universities there and in Canada before arriving in Perth in 1974. Since that time she has been a teacher and researcher in the Department of Anthropology at the University of Western Australia. Her first visit to Japan was in 1983 under a community exchange scheme between Hyogo and Western Australia. In 1992, she took leave without pay for eighteen months to take up the opportunity, with her family, of living and working in Japan. During this time, Hilary taught Australian studies at a women's university in Tokyo.

Angela Snedden is in her fifth year of an Arts–Law degree at the Australian National University. After studying Japanese for a year she went to Japan on a Lions exchange program and fell in love with the country. She returned to Japan for eighteen months on a working holiday after completing the Arts component of her degree, and is planning another trip in 1994.

Cory Taylor graduated from the Australian National University in 1976, after a nomadic childhood and erratic schooling. She abandoned graduate studies at Oxford University to take up writing for film and television in Australia, and later jumped at the opportunity to abandon that for a job teaching English in Japan. Cory lives in Japan and Australia with her Japanese husband and two young children.

Mark Thackray grew up in Sydney and Jakarta before graduating from Macquarie University with a degree in

Mass Communications. He has worked as a baker, an insurance broker, a builder's labourer, a media monitor, a security monitor, a training-film manager, a radio listener surveyor, an organic farmer, a salesman, a bush regenerator and a stuffing-things-into-envelopes person. He also has had stints of being 'occupationally challenged'. Stories of prosperity, adventure and strangeness enticed Mark to Tokyo. He now teaches English somewhere in the Japanese countryside.

Glossary of Japanese Terms

Akira — comic book named after the main character
Amanatsu — citrus fruit
Anime — animated cartoons

Bancha — type of coarse green tea
Banzai — 'hurrah'
Bentô — box lunch
Bessô — country cottage, a weekender
Bodi-con — 'body conscious' girl
Bonsai — potted (dwarf) tree
Buchô — division head
Buraku(min) — people engaged in the abattoir trade, tanning and associated activities, an outsider

Chawan-mushi — savoury steamed egg custard dish

Futon — thick bedquilt/mattress

Gaijin — foreigner
Gaman — endurance, patience
Ganbatte — (*ganbaru*) to persevere, do one's best
Gasshô-zukuri — steep rafter roof
Geisha — professional entertainer
Genkan — front entrance to house

Gochisô-sama — expression used after eating
Gomen nasai — 'I'm sorry'

Hachijo-ben — Hachijo Island dialect
Hai — 'yes', 'all right'
Hazukashii — embarrassed, ashamed
Henro — pilgrim
Hon-chô — city centre, headquarters
Hontô — 'really', 'indeed'

Iie — 'no'
Ikebana — traditional art of floral arrangement
Imo-jôchû — spirit distilled from sweet potatoes
Itadakimasu — expression used before eating

Jama — nuisance, obstruction
Jidai-geki — period adventure drama
Jiko — accident
Jiyûseki — unreserved seating

Kabuki — classical Japanese drama
Kachô-dairi — deputy section head
Kaisha — business organisation/company
Kampai — 'cheers'
Kana — Japanese syllabary (alphabet)
Kanji — Chinese characters
Karaoke — singing to recorded musical backing
Karate — one of the arts of self-defense
Kendô — Japanese martial arts
Kihachijô — silk cloth with yellow, brown and black
           patterns
Kôji — malted rice
Kotatsu — Japanese foot warmer with frame and quilt
           cover

Kudasai — 'please'
Kuroshio — Black Current

Mâbo-dôfu — spicy minced pork and *tôfu* dish
Minshuku — guest-house
Miso — fermented soybean paste
Mizutaki — boiled chicken and vegetable dish
Mizu wari — whiskey and water
Mochi — rice cakes

Nattô — fermented soybeans
Negi — spring onions
Netsuke — small ornaments carved by *samurai*
Nôkyô — agricultural co-operative

O-Bâ-chan — 'grandma'
O-benjo — toilet
O-Bon — 'Festival of the Dead'
O-bôsan — Buddhist monk
O-furo — bath
Ohayô gozaimasu — 'good morning'
O-Jii-chan — 'grandpa'
Okama — transvestite
Omedetô — congratulations
Onigiri — rice balls
Onna — woman, female
O-tearai — toilet
Oyako-don — cooked chicken and eggs over a bowl of rice

Pachinko — pinball game

Râmen — Chinese noodles
Ri — measurement of distance (= approx. 4 kilometres)
Romaji — Japanese written in Roman characters

Runin — exile
Ryokan — Japanese style hotel

Sake — fermented rice wine
Samurai — warrior
Sarariman — white-collar worker
Sashimi — raw fish
Seiza — formal sitting posture
Sensô — war
Shamisen — traditional Japanese three-stringed
          instrument
Shinjinrui — young, trendy person
Shinkansen — 'bullet' train
Shizuka — silent, quiet, tranquil
Shôchû — low grade distilled spirits
Shôji — paper covered sliding screens
Soba — buckwheat noodles
Sukiyaki — thinly sliced beef and vegetables cooked in
          broth
Sumo — traditional wrestling
Sushi (sushiya) — vinegared rice topped with fish or other
          condiments (a *sushi* shop)
Susuki — Japanese pampas grass

Tabemono — food
Tabi — traditional socks
Takai — expensive
Tamaishigaki — retaining walls made with large rounded
          rocks
Tanka — traditional verse of thirty-two syllables
Tatami — straw matting
Teishoku — set menu
Tempura — seafood and vegetables deep fried in batter
Tenchô — club manager

Teppan-yaki — meat and vegetables fried on a hot plate
Tofu — bean curd
Tokkuri — sake bottle
Tomodachi — friend
Tonkatsu — pork cutlet
Tsukubai — stone water-basin
Tsuru — Japanese cranes

Uji iwaii — celebration of birth

Wakarimasen — 'I don't understand/know'
Washoi — 'heave-ho'

Yakitori — grilled chicken
Yakuza — gangsters, Japanese 'mafia'

Zen — Buddhist sect